SCHOLASTIC

QUICK FIX

FOR

YEAR 6

SCIENCE

Stress-busting SATs solutions

Techniques for top marks

30 booster lessons included

Richard Cooper

CREDITS

Author
Richard Cooper

Editors
Ruth Burns
Louise Titley

Series Designer
Anna Oliwa

Designer
Mike Brain Graphic
Design Limited, Oxford

Illustrations
Beverly Curl
Garry Davies

Acknowlegements
Extracts from the
Programmes of Study from
The National Curriculum for
England © Crown copyright
and other Crown copyright
material. Reproduced under
the terms of the Click Use
Licence.

Text © 2007 Richard Cooper
© 2007 Scholastic Ltd

Designed using Adobe InDesign

Published by Scholastic Ltd
Villiers House
Clarendon Avenue
Leamington Spa
Warwickshire CV32 5PR
www.scholastic.co.uk

Printed by Bell and Bain Ltd.

1 2 3 4 5 6 7 8 9   7 8 9 0 1 2 3 4 5 6

British Library Cataloguing-in-Publication Data
A catalogue record for this book is available from the British Library.

ISBN 978-0439-94568-4

CONTENTS

INTRODUCTION.. 4

A GUIDE TO RUNNING BOOSTER LESSONS 6

LETTER TO PARENTS.. 8

BOOSTER LESSON ATTENDANCE REGISTER 9

OBJECTIVES CHART 10

HOW TO REVISE 14

EXAMPLE REVISION TIMETABLE 15

REVISION TIMETABLE TEMPLATE................................ 16

STUDENT PROGRESS CHART..................................... 17

LEVEL 4 PLACEMENT TEST..................................... 18

SELECTING EQUIPMENT 22

FINDING OUT.. 24

PLOTTING GRAPHS 26

PATTERNS IN DATA 28

FAIR TESTING... 30

PREDICTIONS 32

QUESTIONS 34

PLANT GROWTH 36

PARTS OF A FLOWER AND SEED DISPERSAL...................... 38

THE HUMAN SKELETON 40

LIVING PROCESSES 42

CLASSIFICATION 44

KEYS.. 46

ADAPTATION 48

PREDATORS AND THEIR PREY 50

FOOD CHAINS... 52

MICRO-ORGANISMS.. 54

THERMAL INSULATORS AND CONDUCTORS 56

SOLIDS, LIQUIDS AND GASES 58

GROUPING AND CLASSIFYING MATERIALS 60

SEPARATING MIXTURES...................................... 62

MAKING SOLUTIONS 64

GRAVITY... 66

MAGNETS 68

ELECTRICAL CIRCUITS 70

SUN, EARTH AND MOON 72

AIR RESISTANCE 74

FRICTION.. 76

SOUND... 78

LIGHT AND SHADOW 80

SCIENCE CHECKLISTS 82

ANSWERS 87

EXAM TECHNIQUES – HINTS AND TIPS 92

REWARDS AND MOTIVATION................................... 93

INTRODUCTION

Quick Fix for Year 6 Science is designed to support teachers in the build-up to the end-of-year National Tests. It provides everything you will need to organise and run a detailed, structured programme of 'booster lessons' – extra-curricular classes run at lunchtimes or after school which give Year 6 children extra tuition and a chance to review and revise key objectives. Children who successfully complete the programme should go on to achieve a Level 4 or above.

The programme includes:

■ 30 easy-to-follow photocopiable lesson plans with accompanying activity sheets;

■ Lessons designed to make life as easy as possible for the teacher. Minimal preparation is required, yet all the key objectives are covered to achieve a Level 4;

■ A sample placement test at Level 4;

■ Activities that will stretch the more confident learners;

■ A pre-written permission letter to parents;

■ Reward certificates for attendance and achievement;

■ A photocopiable objectives chart for easy teacher reference;

■ Science checklists that can be used as prompts during lessons;

■ Tips and advice for pupils on revision and how to plan their revision time;

■ Hints and tips for success in every lesson;

■ Advice on test technique – both before and during the National Tests.

■ Full answers to all the sample questions;

HOW TO USE THIS BOOK

In order to make the book easy to use, all the lessons follow the same format:

■ What you need – list of resources that can be found in most classrooms;

■ Introduction – a quick and easy start to the lesson;

■ Whole class work – key explanations led by the teacher;

■ Teaching points – three key points for the children to learn in each lesson;

■ Review – review of key learning points and an opportunity for children to present their work;

■ Ideas for homework – using resources commonly found at school;

■ 'Don't panic!' boxes – hints and tips on how to succeed;

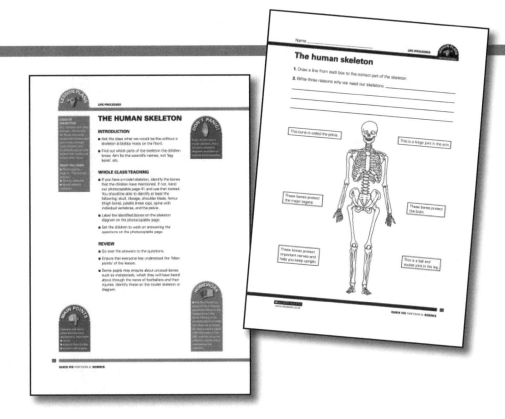

Each lesson is designed to last 20 – 25 minutes allowing them to fit within most school's lunch breaks;

Many worksheets are differentiated. They are divided into three sections: 'Beginner's Bronze', 'Steady Silver' and 'Go for Gold!' The bronze section is pitched within the Level 3 range, the silver overlapping Level 3 and Level 4 and the gold at Levels 4 and 5.

Steady success at the silver level will give a good indication of progress for each child.

The lessons and worksheets are designed to be photocopied at short notice and are designed to be delivered with a minimum of preparation. There are a number of pages that can be photocopied and handed to children for future reference, or to take home and study.

ASSESSING PUPILS' WORK

The sample test can be administered before or after the booster programme. It can be used as a placement test, enabling the teacher to identify gaps in knowledge or areas of strength. Alternatively, after the 30 lessons, the test could give an indication of how much progress has been made over the course of the programme. Any children who are comfortable with the Level 4 test should achieve that level or higher when it comes to the National Tests in May.

A GUIDE TO RUNNING BOOSTER LESSONS

In order to give pupils a chance to prepare properly for the National Tests, it is important to plan the revision period well. Schools differ over when to start revision, but the beginning of the Spring Term is seen by many to be an ideal time.

Here is a 'ten steps to success' guide to get your Year 6 booster lessons up and running quickly and efficiently.

1. Discuss with your pupils what the National Tests are and when they will be taking place (May). Try to instil a sense of team spirit and collective pride. You don't want your pupils to worry about doing badly, but you do want them to be keen to succeed. A common misconception amongst Year 6 pupils is that the levels they achieve in the tests will determine their 'choice' of secondary school. This is a fear that should be laid to rest. For the pupils, the National Tests should be seen as a chance to prove to themselves, to their parents and to the school what they have learnt. Away from the classroom, the pressure is certainly on teachers and headteachers for the Year 6 students to attain the highest possible levels, so taking a responsible and dedicated approach to revision is highly recommended.

2. Introduce the idea of booster lessons to the children. This may not seem like an attractive proposition to some – usually the children who need them the most! You really need that 'pulling together' spirit at the beginning, so it is a good idea to really sell them the idea. You could discuss with the headteacher (who will be very keen to get the best from the pupils) the idea of offering some sort of reward for 100 percent attendance at booster lessons. This could be as a group and/or as individuals. Ideas for rewards include class trips after the National Tests (a game of rounders and a picnic in the park does not cost very much) book/music tokens, or the promise of a day spent playing organised sports tournaments in the playground (see the PE coordinator if need be). Choose something that will appeal to your group.

3. Inform the rest of the staff as soon as possible. Raise the topic of booster lessons at the next staff meeting and rally some support to help you run them. The three core-subject coordinators and members of the senior management team should certainly be involved, but any offers of help from elsewhere would come in very handy. Again, your headteacher should support you here.

4. Timetable the booster lessons so everyone (teachers and pupils) will know when they are taking place. Highlight the available after-school and lunchtime sessions. Try to avoid clashing with popular extra-curricular events such as football club – remember, you need the pupils on side!

5. Aim for the same level of commitment from the Year 6 parents. You can photocopy the permission letter to attend the classes from page 8 or write your own. The parents should welcome the idea, but it is important they support the school by offering incentives at home, as well as ensuring there is a quiet place to work (away from distractions such as siblings and television) and encouraging the completion of homework. Many schools arrange a 'National Tests information evening', when the parents are invited in to ask questions about the tests and raise any concerns. If your headteacher has not arranged this, then ask if it is a possibility.

6. Gather the necessary resources. Your school will have received funds for the purpose of revision, so there should not be a problem with pens, pencils, books and folders. Also, you do not want to waste valuable booster time searching for calculators or retrieving equipment loaned to other classes.

7. Draw up a register of attendance for each booster lesson. You can photocopy the one on page 9 or produce your own.

8. Start the booster lessons with the session on 'How to revise' (see page 12) and ensure that each child has filled in their revision timetable. A photocopiable one is provided on page 14.

9. Establish with the children any rewards which are to be given once the booster lessons and National Tests are over, and lay down the ground rules and expectations.

10. After the first booster lesson (How to revise) ask your headteacher to hold a special assembly to praise the Year 6 students for their commitment, ability and work ethic. They should feel like the 'big kids' of the school and will respond to the notion of providing an example to the younger children. Remember, once they are in Year 7 they will revert to being the 'babies' of their new school, so let them enjoy their status while it lasts!

LETTER TO PARENTS

Dear Parents/Carers,

As you are probably aware, all Year 6 pupils will be taking the Key Stage 2 National Tests for English, Maths and Science in May. These are generally known as SATs and will provide an indication of your child's attainment at the end of their primary school career. We are keen for our pupils to show the best they can do, so in addition to their normal timetable we have organised extra classes known as 'booster lessons'. These will give the pupils a chance to revise the work they have covered over the last three years and hopefully identify and address any gaps in knowledge.

Booster lessons will be taking place during lunch breaks and after school and it would be of great benefit to your child if they could attend as many sessions as possible.

Here is the timetable for these booster lessons, which start on _____ and will run for _____ weeks.

	Monday	Tuesday	Wednesday	Thursday	Friday	After school/ Lunchtime
English						
Math						
Science						

The booster lessons after school will start at _____ pm and finish at _____ pm. Please let us know what arrangements you will be making for your child to get home after these lessons by completing and returning the form below.

With best wishes

Year 6 Teacher(s)

--------------------------------✂--

☐ I give permission for my child to attend booster lessons.

☐ I will arrange for my child to be collected following after-school booster lessons.

☐ My child will be allowed to make their own way home following after-school booster lessons.

Signed _____ (Parent/Carer)

Pupil name _____ Class _____

Please return this form to your child's Year 6 teacher by _____

QUICK FIX FOR YEAR 6: SCIENCE

BOOSTER LESSON ATTENDANCE REGISTER

Subject _____ Teacher in charge _____

Name/Week	1	2	3	4	5	6	7	8	9	10	11	Permission slip	Getting home

SCHOLASTIC
www.scholastic.co.uk

QUICK FIX FOR YEAR 6: SCIENCE

OBJECTIVES CHART

QUICK FIX LESSON	OBJECTIVES
Selecting equipment (pages 22–23)	**Sc1: Scientific enquiry** **Investigative skills** *Obtaining and presenting evidence* **2e.** Pupils should be taught to use simple equipment and materials appropriately and take action to control risks
Finding out (pages 24–25)	**Sc1: Scientific enquiry** **Ideas and evidence in science** **1a.** Pupils should be taught that science is about thinking creatively to try to explain how living and non-living things work, and to establish links between causes and effects **Investigative skills** **2b.** Pupils should be taught to consider what sources of information, including first-hand experience and a range of other sources, they will use to answer questions
Plotting graphs (pages 26–27)	**Sc1: Scientific enquiry** **Investigative skills** *Obtaining and presenting evidence* **2h.** Pupils should be taught to use a wide range of methods, including diagrams, drawings, table, bar charts, line graphs and ICT, to communicate data in an appropriate and systematic manner
Patterns in data (pages 28–29)	**Sc1: Scientific enquiry** **Investigative skills** *Considering evidence and evaluating* **2** Pupils should be taught to: **i.** make comparisons and identify simple patterns or associations in their own observations and measurements or other data **j.** use observations, measurements or other data to draw conclusions **k.** decide whether these conclusions agree with any prediction made and/or whether they enable further predictions to be made
Fair testing (pages 30–31)	**Sc1: Scientific enquiry** **Investigative skills** **2d.** Pupils should be taught to make a fair test or comparison by changing one factor and observing or measuring the effect while keeping the other factors the same
Predictions (pages 32–33)	**Sc1: Scientific enquiry** **Investigative skills** *Considering evidence and evaluating* **2.** Pupils should be taught to **j.** use observations, measurements or other data to draw conclusions **k.** decide whether these conclusions agree with any prediction made and/or whether they enable further predictions to be made

Questions (pages 34–35)	**Sc1: Scientific enquiry** **Investigative skills** **2a.** Pupils should be taught to ask questions that can be investigated scientifically and decide how to find answers
Plant growth (pages 36–37)	**Sc2: Life processes and living things** **Green plants** **3.** Pupils should be taught **a.** the effect of light, air water and temperature on plant growth **b.** the role of the leaf in producing new material for growth **c.** that the root anchors the plant, and that water and minerals are taken in through the root and transported through the stem to other parts of the plant
Parts of a flower and seed dispersal (pages 38–39)	**Sc2: Life processes and living things** **Green plants – Reproduction** **3d.** Pupils should be taught the parts of the flower and their role in the life cycle of flowering plants, including pollination, seed formation, seed dispersal and germination
The human skeleton (pages 40–41)	**Sc2: Life processes and living things** **Humans and other animals – Movement** **2e.** Pupils should be taught that humans and some other animals have skeletons and muscles to support and protect their bodies and to help them to move
Living processes (pages 42–43)	**Sc2: Life processes and living things** **Life processes** **1.** Pupils should be taught: **a.** that the life processes common to humans and other animals include nutrition, movement, growth and reproduction **b.** that the life processes common to plants include growth, nutrition and reproduction
Classification (pages 44–45)	**Sc2: Life processes and living things** **Variation and classification** **4c.** Pupils should be taught that the variety of plants and animals makes it important to identify them and assign them to groups
Keys (pages 46–47)	**Sc2: Life processes and living things** **Variation and classification** **4a.** Pupils should be taught how to make and use keys
Adaptation (pages 48–49)	**Sc2: Life processes and living things** **Living things in their environment – Feeding relationships** **5.** Pupils should be taught: **b.** about the different plants and animals found in different habitats **c.** how animals and plants in two different habitats are suited to their environment

Predators and their prey (pages 50–51)	**Sc2: Life processes and living things** **Living things in their environment – Feeding relationships** **5d.** Pupils should be taught to use food chains to show feeding relationships in a habitat
Food chains (pages 52–53)	**Sc2: Life processes and living things** **Living things in their environment – Feeding relationships** **5e.** Pupils should be taught about how nearly all food chains start with a green plant
Micro-organisms (pages 54–55)	**Sc2: Life processes and living things** **Living things in their environment – Micro-organisms** **5f.** Pupils should be taught that micro-organisms are living organisms that are often too small to be seen, and that they may be beneficial or harmful
Thermal insulators and conductors (pages 56–57)	**Sc3: Materials and their properties** **Grouping and classifying materials** **1b.** Pupils should be taught that some materials are better thermal insulators than others
Solids, liquids and gases (pages 58–59)	**Sc3: Materials and their properties** **Grouping and classifying materials** **1e.** Pupils should be taught to recognise differences between solids, liquids and gases, in terms of ease of flow and maintenance of shape and volume
Grouping and classifying materials (pages 60–61)	**Sc3: Materials and their properties** **Grouping and classifying materials** **1a.** Pupils should be taught to compare everyday materials and objects on the basis of their material properties, including hardness, strength, flexibility and magnetic behaviour, and to relate these properties to everyday uses of the materials
Separating mixtures (pages 62–63)	**Sc3: Materials and their properties** **Separating mixtures of materials** **3.** Pupils should be taught: **a.** how to separate solid particles of different sizes by sieving **c.** how to separate insoluble solids from liquids by filtering **d.** how to recover dissolved solids by evaporating the liquid from the solution
Making solutions (pages 64–65)	**Sc3: Materials and their properties** **Separating mixtures of materials** **3b.** Pupils should be taught that some solids dissolve in water to give solutions but some do not
Gravity (pages 66–67)	**Sc4: Physical processes** **Forces and motion** **2.** Pupils should be taught: **b.** that objects are pulled downwards because of the gravitational attraction between them and the Earth **e.** how to measure forces and identify the direction in which they act

Magnets (pages 67–68)	**Sc4: Physical processes** **Forces and motion** **2a.** Pupils should be taught about the forces of attraction and repulsion between magnets, and about the forces of attraction between magnets and magnetic materials
Electrical circuits (pages 70–71)	**Sc4: Physical processes** **Electricity** **1c.** Pupils should be taught how to represent series circuits by drawings and conventional symbols, and how to construct series circuits on the basis of drawings and diagrams using conventional symbols
Sun, Earth and the Moon (pages 72–73)	**Sc4: Physical processes** **The Earth and beyond** **4.** Pupils should be taught: **a.** that the Sun, Earth and Moon are approximately spherical **Periodic changes** **c.** how day and night are related to the spin of the Earth on its own axis **d.** that the Earth orbits the Sun once each year, and that the Moon takes approximately 28 days to orbit the Earth
Air resistance (pages 74–75)	**Sc4: Physical processes** **Forces and motion** **2c.** Pupils should be taught about friction, including air resistance, as a force that slows moving objects and may prevent objects from starting to move
Friction (pages 76–77)	**Sc4: Physical processes** **Forces and motion** **2c.** Pupils should be taught about friction, including air resistance, as a force that slows moving objects and may prevent objects from starting to move
Sound (pages 78–79)	**Sc4: Physical processes** **Light and sound – Vibration and sound** **3.** Pupils should be taught: **e.** that sounds are made when objects vibrate but that vibrations are not always directly visible **g.** that vibrations from sound sources require a medium through which to travel to the ear
Light and shadow (pages 80–81)	**Sc4: Physical processes** **Light and sound** **3.** Pupils should be taught: **a.** that light travels from a source **b.** that light cannot pass through some materials, and how this leads to the formation of shadows **c.** that light is reflected from surfaces

HOW TO REVISE

You will need a copy of the revision timetable example (page 15) and a blank version (page 16) for each pupil.

INTRODUCTION

- Inform the pupils about your plans for them as a group over the coming weeks. Tell them who will be teaching them, and where and when they will be taught.

- Establish your expectations from the start. Regular attendance and cooperative behaviour should be the minimum requirements from all pupils coming to the booster lessons.

- Explain to the pupils that this first session is to help them organise themselves and prepare properly by establishing a revision routine and timetable.

- Tell the pupils that revision work is reinforcing learning and filling any gaps in knowledge. They shouldn't be tackling concepts which are completely alien, although some children may find they may have missed certain topics through lengthy absences. This is their (and your) chance to rectify these points.

WHOLE CLASS TEACHING

- Discuss suitable places to work at home. Somewhere quiet where you are unlikely to be disturbed and somewhere you can keep your books and equipment laid out is ideal – for example, a desk in your bedroom.

- Discuss when to work. 'Little and often' should be the tactic here. Three 15-minute sessions throughout the day can be more beneficial than an hour slumped over a textbook before bed.

- Discuss what to work on. Explain that the whole group will be working on a prepared plan of action.

- Hand out a copy of the example revision timetable on page 15 and discuss with the group any issues that may arise.

- Hand out a copy of the blank revision timetable on page 16 for each child to fill in. They need to plan for the subject they are studying and indeed the other two core-subject booster lessons if they are attending those as well.

- Pupils need to keep the timetables somewhere easily accessible. If they have a booster lesson folder, perhaps they could attach it to the inside cover.

REVIEW

- To finish the session, the pupils could share their ideas on mixing leisure and revision time.

- You may want to encourage your pupils to pair up as 'revision buddies'. They could support each other out of class by doing homework together.

EXAMPLE REVISION TIMETABLE

	Monday	Tuesday	Wednesday	Thursday	Friday	Saturday	Sunday
7.00am	Key facts – Maths 10 mins	Key facts – Science 10 mins	Key facts – English 10 mins	Key facts – Maths 10 mins	Key facts – Science 10 mins	Key facts – English 10 mins	Sleep
8.00am							Sleep
9.00am	Numeracy hour	Numeracy hour	Numeracy hour	Numeracy hour	Numeracy hour		
10.00am	Literacy hour	Literacy hour	Literacy hour	Literacy hour	Literacy hour	Play football	Swimming
11.00am		Science		Science			
12.00pm		12.30 – Science booster	12.30 – Maths booster	12.30 – Science booster	12.30 – English booster		
1.00pm							Sunday lunch
2.00pm			PE		Art class	Shopping	Walk the dog
3.00pm	3.30 – Maths booster		3.30 – English booster				
4.00pm				Guitar lesson		Bike ride	
5.00pm							English homework
6.00pm	Maths homework	Science homework	English homework	Maths homework	Science homework	Cinema	TV
7.00pm	Spellings		Spellings		Maths vocabulary		
8.00pm	Read/bed	Read/bed	Read/bed	Read/bed	Read/bed		Read/bed

Name _____

REVISION TIMETABLE

	7.00am	8.00am	9.00am	10.00am	11.00am	12.00pm	1.00pm	2.00pm	3.00pm	4.00pm	5.00pm	6.00pm	7.00pm	8.00pm
Monday														
Tuesday														
Wednesday														
Thursday														
Friday														
Saturday														
Sunday														

QUICK FIX FOR YEAR 6: SCIENCE

SCHOLASTIC
www.scholastic.co.uk

STUDENT PROGRESS CHART

OBJECTIVE	BRONZE	SILVER	GOLD
Sc1 Selecting equipment			
Sc1 Finding out			
Sc1 Plotting graphs			
Sc1 Patterns in data			
Sc1 Fair testing			
Sc1 Predictions			
Sc1 Questions			
Sc1 Investigations			
Sc2 Flowers and seed dispersal			
Sc2 The human skeleton			
Sc2 Living processes			
Sc2 Classification			
Sc2 Keys			
Sc2 Adaptation			
Sc2 Predators and their prey			
Sc2 Food chains			
Sc2 Micro-organisms			
Sc3 Insulators and conductors			
Sc3 Solids, liquids and gases			
Sc3 Grouping materials			
Sc3 Separating mixtures			
Sc3 Making mixtures			
Sc4 Forces and motion			
Sc4 Magnets			
Sc4 Electrical circuits			
Sc4 Sun, Earth and the Moon			
Sc4 Air resistance			
Sc4 Friction			
Sc4 Sound			
Sc4 Light and shadows			

LEVEL 4 PLACEMENT TEST

This test is based around 'scientific enquiry', which features heavily in the KS2 National Tests. It covers the four areas of the NC Programme of Study for science. The questions are typical of those that you will answer in a standard National Test paper.

GYROCOPTERS

Class 6A are testing gyrocopters of different sizes made from the same type of paper.

1. What were Class 6A trying to find out? (Tick one box.)

   a. Do heavy gyrocopters fall slowly? ☐

   b. Do smaller gyrocopters fall very quickly? ☐

   c. Is paper a good material to use to make a gyrocopter? ☐

   d. Do large gyrocopters fall slower than smaller ones? ☐

2. Here is a table showing Class 6A's results from the investigation.

Length of wings on the gyrocopter	Time taken to touch the ground
4cm	2 seconds
6cm	4 seconds
8cm	5 seconds

Study the results and tick the box beside the correct statement.

   a. All the gyrocopters took the same time to reach the ground. ☐

   b. Gyrocopters with longer wings fall more slowly. ☐

   c. Gyrocopters with shorter wings fall more slowly. ☐

3. Class 6A then repeated their investigation and added two extra paper clips to each gyrocopter. What do you think the results showed this time? (Tick one box.)

   a. The gyrocopters spun faster and took longer to reach the ground. ☐

   b. The results stayed the same. ☐

   c. The gyrocopters all reached the ground in a shorter space of time. ☐

4. Write two things Class 6A needed to keep the same during the investigation.

☐
☐
☐
☐

TOTAL

☐

Marks for page = 5

Name ______________________

PRACTICE TEST
PHOTOCOPIABLE

OUR PLANET

5. Hundreds of years ago, sailors were afraid of sailing too far and falling off the edge the world. They thought the world was flat. What shape is planet Earth?

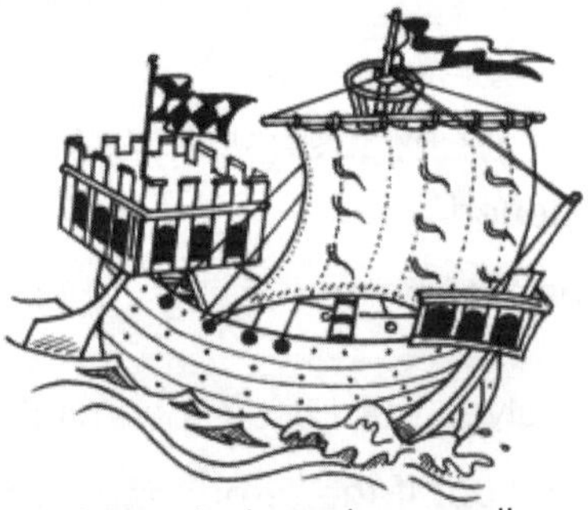

6. Scientists in the past also had different views about their understanding of the Sun and the Earth. Some of them were correct, others we now know were not.

Which of these statements are true?

Idea	True	False
The Earth is the centre of the universe.		
The Sun orbits the Earth.		
The Earth spins on its axis.		
The Sun is the largest planet.		
The Earth orbits the Sun.		
Night is dark because the fire in the Sun goes out.		

7. This diagram shows rain clouds over different parts of planet Earth. It is just about to start raining.

Draw an arrow from each cloud to show the direction of gravity acting on the raindrops.

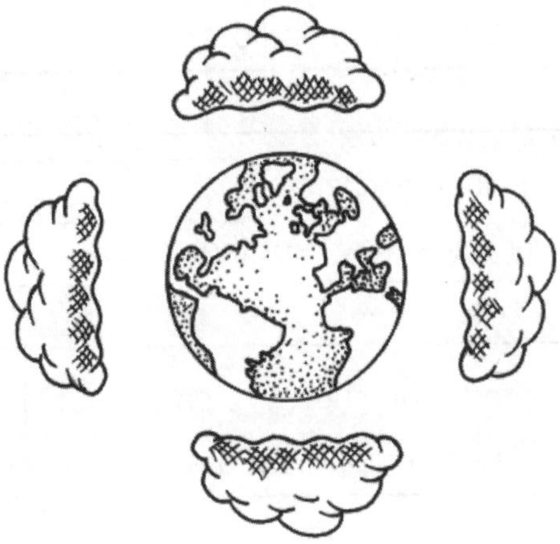

8. Write an explanation for your answer to question 7 and include the word 'gravity'.

TOTAL

Marks for page = 9

SCHOLASTIC
www.scholastic.co.uk

Name _____

DISSOLVING

Class 6A carried out an investigation into how quickly sugar dissolves in water.

This is what happened.

- They found that a teaspoon of sugar took hours to dissolve if they did not stir it.
- The sugar dissolved quickest if the solution was constantly stirred.

They wanted to find out if the temperature of the water made a difference.

- They used water from the hot and cold taps to get different temperatures.
- They used three teaspoons of sugar each time.
- They used 100ml of water each time.
- The same person stirred each mixture constantly and at the same speed.
- They timed how long it took for the sugar to completely disappear.
- James made a prediction:
  'I predict that the sugar will dissolve quicker the hotter the water.'

  Here are their results.

Temperature of water	Time taken to dissolve (seconds)
15°C	175
25°C	118
35°C	63
45°C	27

9. What did Class 6A want to find out?

10. Which variable did they change?

11. Name three variables they kept the same.

12. Was James's prediction shown to be correct?

13. Name three items of equipment they would have used.

14. Give one reason why they did not use boiling water.

15. What conclusion did 6A arrive at?

TOTAL

Marks for page = 7

HABITATS

Some children from Class 6A used the internet and library to research different habitats. They listed three plants or animals that lived in each one. These are the findings for each pupil:

George: *gazelle, baobab tree, cheetah*
Chantelle: *gerbil, rattlesnake, cactus*
Grace: *toucan, jaguar, orchid*
Jackson: *parrotfish, sea cucumber, turf algae*
Rosie: *sandpiper, Brent goose, salt-marsh grass*
Kevin: *Douglas fir, yak, alpine hare*

Habitat	Pupil name
Rainforest	
Desert	
Coral reef	
Grassland	
Mountain region	
River estuary	

16. Write the correct pupil name next to each habitat.

17. The squirrel has adapted to living in trees by having sharp claws for climbing and a long tail for balancing.

List one way each of these animals has adapted to its habitat.

Animal	Habitat	Adaptation
Polar bear	Arctic circle	
Gibbon	Rainforest	
Giraffe	Savannah	

Marks for page = 9

Total marks for test = _____/30

□ □

TOTAL

□

SELECTING EQUIPMENT

INTRODUCTION

- Ask the class whether they think selecting the correct equipment for a scientific experiment is important. Ask: *What could happen if the wrong equipment is used?*

- Ask the class what equipment they would need to find out which materials conduct electricity. Write down their ideas on a piece of sugar paper. Discuss the responses and record on the sugar paper in bullet points or in a 'brainstorm' style.

- You should arrive at a list that contains something like the following: a battery (cell), bulb, switch, connecting wires, crocodile clips and materials to test.

- Display the 'poster' during the lesson.

WHOLE CLASS TEACHING

- Hand out a copy of photocopiable page 22 to each pupil.

- Go through question 1 as a group.

- Ask the class which items of equipment they might need to be careful with. Are there any health and safety issues? Discuss this as a group.

- Set the class to work on the remainder of the worksheet.

REVIEW

- Go through the remainder of the worksheet with the class and discuss the answers.

- Make any additions to the class poster that might have arisen.

OBJECTIVE
Sc1: Investigative skills – Obtaining and presenting evidence 2e. Pupils should be taught to use simple equipment and materials appropriately and take action to control risks

WHAT YOU NEED
- Photocopiable page 23 'Selecting equipment'
- Writing materials
- Sugar paper and marker pen

- Scientific enquiry questions will appear in the National Tests. They will usually be based around a picture or description of an experiment. You will probably be asked questions about the results of that experiment.
- You do not actually do the experiment, but you might be asked how you would improve it, were you to perform it in class.

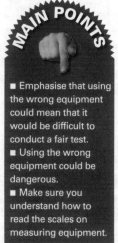

- Emphasise that using the wrong equipment could mean that it would be difficult to conduct a fair test.
- Using the wrong equipment could be dangerous.
- Make sure you understand how to read the scales on measuring equipment.

- Discuss with your revision buddy the items of equipment you have used when conducting different experiments and investigations.

Selecting equipment

1. Match the equipment to the units of measurement.
Draw a line from each piece of equipment to the appropriate unit of measurement.

stopwatch	millilitres
weighing scales	minutes and seconds
forcemeter	grams
ruler	Newtons
tape measure	degrees Celsius
thermometer	millimetres
measuring jug	metres

2. Charlie wants to measure how high a basketball bounces when he drops it on to different surfaces from various heights. What measuring equipment should he use?

3. Charlie also wants to investigate how quickly a spinner falls to the floor. Write the name of one piece of equipment he could use to measure this.

4. Emma measures the weight of a stone in air and then in a bucket of water. Write the name of the measuring equipment she should use to do this.

5. On the back of this sheet, write down the equipment you would need to bring back a rock sample from Mars.

■ SCHOLASTIC
www.scholastic.co.uk

FINDING OUT

INTRODUCTION

■ Ask the class what they have 'found out' recently.

■ Write the best answers on the sugar paper.

■ Discuss how they came to find these things out.

WHOLE CLASS TEACHING

■ Discuss famous scientists and how they worked on their discoveries and inventions. Ideas to follow up using the internet and the library include:

■ Isaac Newton and the laws of gravity

■ Marie Curie discovering radium and winning two Nobel prizes

■ Louis Pasteur and pasteurisation

■ Edward Jenner and the invention of vaccination

■ Leonardo da Vinci and the ideas in his notebooks

■ Charles Darwin and his theory of evolution

■ Keep this to a teacher and class discussion or set group-tasks to complete. For example: *Helen, Shaun and Amy, I'd like you to use the library and find out three interesting facts about Charles Darwin and report back to the group in ten minutes.*

REVIEW

■ Bring the groups together to discuss their findings.

Finding out

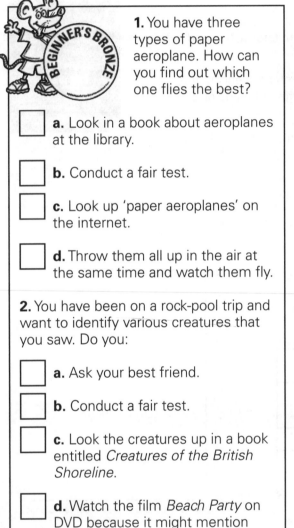

1. You have three types of paper aeroplane. How can you find out which one flies the best?

☐ **a.** Look in a book about aeroplanes at the library.

☐ **b.** Conduct a fair test.

☐ **c.** Look up 'paper aeroplanes' on the internet.

☐ **d.** Throw them all up in the air at the same time and watch them fly.

2. You have been on a rock-pool trip and want to identify various creatures that you saw. Do you:

☐ **a.** Ask your best friend.

☐ **b.** Conduct a fair test.

☐ **c.** Look the creatures up in a book entitled *Creatures of the British Shoreline*.

☐ **d.** Watch the film *Beach Party* on DVD because it might mention rock pools.

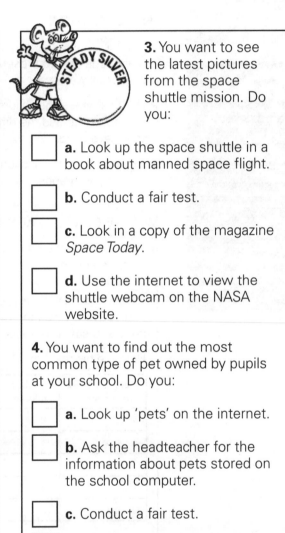

3. You want to see the latest pictures from the space shuttle mission. Do you:

☐ **a.** Look up the space shuttle in a book about manned space flight.

☐ **b.** Conduct a fair test.

☐ **c.** Look in a copy of the magazine *Space Today*.

☐ **d.** Use the internet to view the shuttle webcam on the NASA website.

4. You want to find out the most common type of pet owned by pupils at your school. Do you:

☐ **a.** Look up 'pets' on the internet.

☐ **b.** Ask the headteacher for the information about pets stored on the school computer.

☐ **c.** Conduct a fair test.

☐ **d.** Conduct a school survey.

Choose a famous scientist that you have come across in the lesson or you have heard about of before. Do as much research as you can on their life's work and achievements. Present your findings as a poster, booklet, tape-recording or word-processed document.

SCHOLASTIC
www.scholastic.co.uk

QUICK FIX FOR YEAR 6: SCIENCE

PLOTTING GRAPHS

LESSON OBJECTIVE
Sc1: Investigative skills – Obtaining and presenting evidence 2h. Pupils are taught to use a wide range of methods, including diagrams, drawings, table, bar charts, line graphs and ICT, to communicate data in an appropriate and systematic manner

WHAT YOU NEED
■ Photocopiable page 27, 'Plotting graphs'
■ Writing materials
■ A pre-prepared graph (see below) drawn on sugar paper as a poster, or drawn on the board.

INTRODUCTION

■ Ask the class what they think is the purpose of a graph (primarily to present information and data in a visual way).

■ Discuss where the children have encountered graphs before and the different types of graph they have used.

■ Explain that in this lesson they will be learning how to plot graphs.

WHOLE CLASS TEACHING

■ Work through the graph question below, displayed on the board.

Raj conducted a survey to find out which was the most popular break time snack.

Here are his results:

Preferred break-time snack	Number of children
Biscuit	28
Banana	21
Cereal bar	35
Seeds	4
Orange	17

Plot the results on this bar chart.

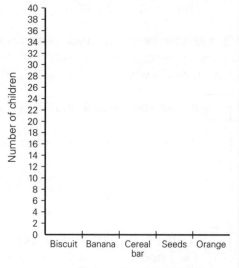

■ Set the class to work on photocopiable page 27.

REVIEW

■ Go through the answers to the three questions on the photocopiable page.

■ Identify any common problems the group may have had. If they are all successful then they are on the way to a Level 4 or beyond!

■ Make sense of a question before trying to answer it. Read the information given carefully and study any graphs and charts. Can you see the connection between the two?

■ Label the axes correctly.
■ When plotting points, be accurate and use a sharp pencil.
■ Mark scales on graphs in an economical way. For example, if the largest piece of data is '16' then the scale should be something like 0 to 20, not 0 to 100.

■ The children can find examples of graphs in newspapers and magazines. (Climate change offers plenty of data.) They should read them and make sense of the information that is presented.

Plotting graphs

Dylan investigated the rate at which ice cubes melted. Draw a bar chart to show his results.

Type of insulation	Number of minutes ice took to melt
Tissue paper	12
None	10
Foil	16
Cotton	15
Bubble wrap	19

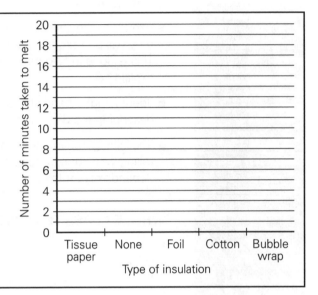

Bruce did a survey for the school football club. Label the slices of this pie chart showing his information.

Main kicking foot	Number of people in the football club
Left	10
Right	15
Both	5

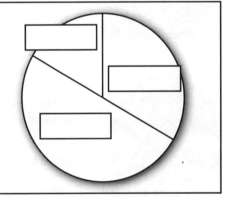

Mark these points on this graph and draw a line to connect them. Patti planted a potato plant and measured its rate of growth.

Week	Height of potato plant (cm)
1	0
2	5
3	10
4	15
5	25
6	35

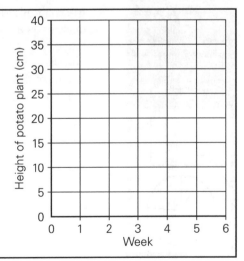

PATTERNS IN DATA

LESSON OBJECTIVES

Sc1: Investigative skills – Considering evidence and evaluating

2 Pupils are taught to:

i. make comparisons and identify simple patterns or associations in their own observations and measurements or other data

j. use observations, measurements or other data to draw conclusions

k. decide whether these conclusions agree with any prediction made and/or whether they enable further predictions to be made

WHAT YOU NEED

■ Photocopiable page 28, 'Patterns in data'

■ Writing materials

INTRODUCTION

■ Explain to the children that to achieve a Level 4 they will be asked to interpret patterns in data. This is done in two main ways: identifying and explaining.

■ 'Identifying' means successfully reading and describing the data in charts and graphs.

■ 'Explaining' means describing what that data is telling you. For example, saying that one factor depends on another.

WHOLE CLASS TEACHING

■ Hand out photocopiable page 28 and ask the children to look at the first graph. Tell the class that they are going to look at identifying data first.

■ Ask the following questions:

1. What is this graph showing us? (How far a toy car rolled on a smooth wooden floor, after coming down a ramp.)
2. How far did the car roll when the ramp was at 10cm high? (75cm)
3. How high was the ramp when the car rolled 45cm? (6cm high)

■ Tell the children that they are now going to look at explaining patterns in the data.

■ Ask the children to look at the first graph again and explain what the data is telling them. Write the children's descriptions on the board and discuss as a group. Aim for something like: The higher the ramp, the further the toy car rolled. The distance the toy car rolled depended on the height of the ramp. The pattern would continue if the ramp kept increasing in height.

■ Ask the children to complete graph 2 using the data in the table. Remind them that this time, the toy car rolled on at carpeted floor. How does this affect the data?

REVIEW

■ Confirm that the children know the difference between identifying data and explaining data.

■ Look for easy patterns and describe them.

■ There are two main sorts of graphs and charts that show this type of information: bar graphs and pie charts. The taller the bar or the larger the slice of pie, the greater the amount of whatever is being measured.

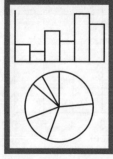

Patterns in data

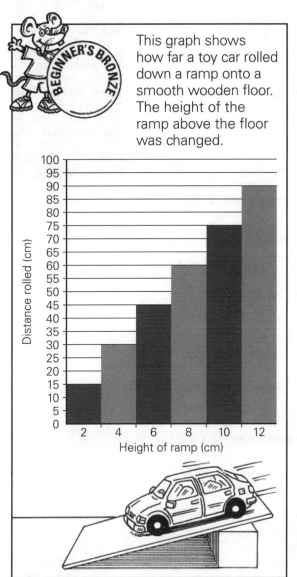

This graph shows how far a toy car rolled down a ramp onto a smooth wooden floor. The height of the ramp above the floor was changed.

This data shows how far a toy car rolled down a ramp onto a carpeted floor. Complete the bar chart using the data in the table.

Height of ramp	2cm	4cm	6cm	8cm	10cm	12cm
Distance travelled	4cm	5cm	7cm	10cm	15cm	23cm

Look at the pattern in the data above, and make a prediction of how far you think the car would travel if the ramp was raised to 16cm. What do you think would happen if the ramp was raised almost vertically? Discuss with a partner.

FAIR TESTING

LESSON OBJECTIVE

Sc1: Investigative skills 2d. Pupils should be taught to make a fair test or comparison by changing one factor and observing or measuring the effect while keeping the other factors the same

WHAT YOU NEED

■ Photocopiable page 31, 'Fair Testing'
■ Writing materials
■ One large ball (e.g. football) and one small ball (e.g. marble)

INTRODUCTION

■ Scientists always test theories by changing the factors involved.

WHOLE CLASS TEACHING

■ Say the class is going to conduct a fair test.

■ Ask: *Do heavy things fall faster than light things?*

■ Ask them to predict what will happen if a large football and a small ball are dropped from the same height. *Will the larger ball reach the ground first?*

■ Most of the class will probably say the football.

■ Say: In around 1590 Galileo Galilei (1564–1642) climbed the Leaning Tower of Pisa and dropped two objects. Two balls of different masses, but similar shape and density were released together and hit the ground at the same time.

Until then it was believed that heavy things fell faster than light things – if you drop a brick and a feather at the same time, the brick will hit the ground first. However this is because of differences in the amount of friction between these objects and the air around them, not because their masses are different. If this test was conducted on the Moon (in a vacuum), the feather and the brick would hit the ground at the same time.

■ Now conduct the experiment holding the two balls high above your head at the same height. Ask: *Has anyone changed their mind?* (The balls will hit the ground at the same time if released simultaneously.)

■ Now repeat the experiment standing on a table. Ask: *What variable has been changed?* (The height from which the balls were dropped.)

■ Are the results the same or different?

■ The class write up the experiment on photocopiable page 31.

REVIEW

■ Read out some of the write-ups of the experiment. Has everyone reached the same conclusions?

■ Scientific tests have to be fair to be valid.
■ You can make a test fair by changing one factor and noting the effect while keeping all the other factors the same.
■ Never assume something; always question and test your ideas!

Fair testing

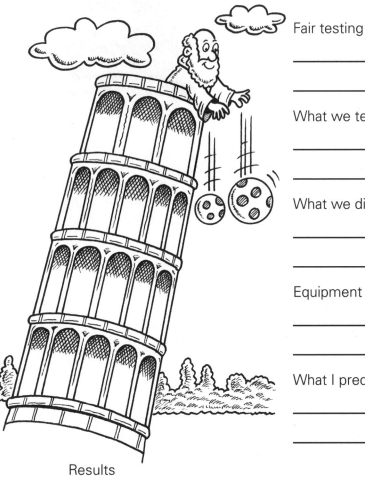

Fair testing

_____

_____

What we tested

_____

_____

What we did

_____

_____

Equipment used

_____

_____

What I predicted

_____

_____

Results

_____

_____

What did we change?

_____

_____

What stayed the same?

_____

_____

Conclusion

_____

_____

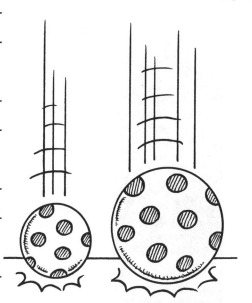

PREDICTIONS

INTRODUCTION

- Ask the children what they think a prediction is.

- Establish that a scientific prediction is based on known evidence and patterns in data – not wild guesses or ideas like horoscopes!

- Some predictions will always be correct, e.g. the sun will rise in the morning. Others will always be wrong, e.g. King Kong will become the new headteacher.

- Ask: *What is the difference between these predictions?* (There is irrefutable evidence that the sun rises every morning; King Kong meanwhile would not be able to handle this class!)

WHOLE CLASS TEACHING

- Discuss weather forecasts with the class: *What is the weather like now? What will the weather be like tomorrow? What is your prediction based on? How do weather forecasters predict the weather? What instruments do they use? How accurate can they be?*

- Set the children to work on the questions on photocopiable page 33.

REVIEW

- Go over the questions on the worksheet with the class.

- To finish, try this psychological prediction to amaze your class. (Hopefully!) Tell them you are going to predict a word that the majority of them will write down. Hidden from the class, write the word 'carrot' in large letters on a piece of paper and conceal it theatrically. Ask them a series of easy questions, which they can all answer by calling out. ('What's 2 + 2?' etc.) After they have got into a rhythm, ask them to quickly write down the first vegetable they can think of. Most will write 'carrot'. Slowly reveal your word…you will be revered as a teacher with special powers! (If it doesn't work you'll have to make up your own excuse!)

LESSON OBJECTIVES

Sc1: Investigative skills – Considering evidence and evaluating
2. Pupils should be taught to:
j. use observations, measurements or other data to draw conclusions
k. decide whether these conclusions agree with any prediction made and/or whether they enable any further predictions to be made

WHAT YOU NEED

- Photocopiable page 33, 'Predictions'
- Writing materials

- Remember, a prediction should be 'an informed guess'.

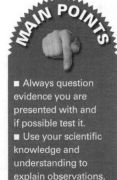

- Always question evidence you are presented with and if possible test it.
- Use your scientific knowledge and understanding to explain observations, measurements or other data and conclusions.
- Use your imagination – picture what you think will happen during an experiment beforehand.

HOMEWORK

- Study the local weather forecast in the newspapers and on television and radio. Based on the different reports, write three predictions about the weather for the coming weekend. Later review how accurate your predictions were.

Predictions

1. Scarlett and Martin ran a cross-country race. They measured their pulse rates before and after the race. Their pulse rates increased during the race. Afterwards, they sat down and rested. Predict what happened to their pulse rates over the next 10 minutes.
Scarlett and Martin's pulse rates will...

2. Scarlett is testing the strength of different kitchen rolls. Her teacher asks her to predict which make of kitchen roll will be the strongest. What factor do you think Scarlett should think about? (Tick one box only.)

- [ ] **a.** The colour of the roll.
- [ ] **b.** The ink used in the design.
- [ ] **c.** The thickness of the paper.

3. Scarlett now has to decide which forcemeter she is going to use to test the strength of each kitchen roll. She has a choice of three. Which one should she choose? (Tick one box.)

- [ ] **a.** A forcemeter which measures up to 1000 Newtons (100kg)
- [ ] **b.** A forcemeter which measures up to 100 Newtons (10kg)
- [ ] **c.** A forcemeter which measures up to 10 Newtons (1kg)

4. Scarlett repeats the experiment but this time she wants to see if the different kitchen rolls are stronger when wet. What is your prediction?
I think...

5. Scarlett and three friends each examined a different type of paper towel.
Scarlett: *Wiper* towels are rough with bits in.
Martin: *Soaker* towels have three layers and a flowery design.
Vicky: *Mopper* towels have five layers so I think they will absorb more water than the others.
Laura: *Spilter* towels are thin and flexible.

a. Who made a prediction?

b. What did the others make?

QUESTIONS

INTRODUCTION

■ Tell the class that to reach Level 4 they have to be able to decide how to investigate the answers to questions in a scientific way.

WHOLE CLASS TEACHING

■ Ask the class the following question: *Do large parachutes fall more slowly than small parachutes?* Discuss the responses.

■ Ask: *How can we find out the answer to the question?*

■ Write this possible answer on the board:

Hussein cut three pieces of plastic from a large bin liner and made three parachutes of the same shape. He attached a 10g weight to each one and dropped them from the same height. Here are his results.

Size of parachute	Time taken to reach the ground
100cm^2	2.5 seconds
225cm^2	3.8 seconds
400cm^2	5.2 seconds

■ Ask the class whether they can now answer the question. What conclusion can you draw from the results of the test? Was the test fair? (The results show that the larger the area of the parachute, the longer it takes to reach the ground, so yes, large parachutes do fall more slowly than small ones. The test was fair because all the factors were constant, except the size of the plastic used for the parachutes.)

■ Set the class to work on photocopiable page 34.

REVIEW

■ Go over the answers to photocopiable page 34 and discuss any points which the class might raise.

Questions

1. What was Hussein trying to find out about parachutes? (Tick only one box.)

☐ **a.** Whether plastic parachutes are better than cotton ones.

☐ **b.** Whether plastic parachutes should be used by sky-divers.

☐ **c.** Whether large parachutes fall more slowly than small ones.

☐ **d.** Whether black parachutes fall more slowly than green ones.

2. Which of these questions could be answered in a scientific way by conducting an investigation? (Tick two boxes.)

☐ **a.** What is your favourite pizza topping?

☐ **b.** Which football team do you support?

☐ **c.** What is the most popular pizza topping in our school?

☐ **d.** Which metals are attracted to magnets?

3. Write three questions that can be answered through conducting a scientific investigation.

4. Draw a diagram and make notes of an investigation to test which of three different brands was the best washing powder out – 'Sudz', 'Gleamo' or 'Stainzap'.

PLANT GROWTH

LESSON OBJECTIVE

Sc2: Green plants
3. Pupils should be taught:
a. The effect of light, air, water and temperature on plant growth
b. The role of the leaf in producing new material for growth
c. That the root anchors the plant, and that water and minerals are taken in through the root and transported through the stem to other parts of the plant

WHAT YOU NEED

■ Photocopiable page 37, 'Plant-growth quiz'
■ Writing materials
■ A stick of celery, a jar of water and some food colouring (optional)

INTRODUCTION

■ To achieve Level 4 you need to know how different parts of a plant work.

■ For this lesson we are going to learn some facts about plants and then hold a quiz.

WHOLE CLASS TEACHING

■ Write these facts about plant growth on the board and go through each one with the class:

  ■ Water – All plants need water (as do all living things).

  ■ Roots – take water and nutrients from the soil and transport them to the stem and other parts of the plant. Roots also anchor the plant.

  ■ Stem – Water and nutrients travel through the stem to other parts of the plant.

  ■ Leaves – make food for the plant (…through photosynthesis. If the group are able to understand the process then explain it to them. This is Level 5 work.)

■ Give the class a few minutes to digest these facts and ask any questions.

■ Cover up the board and set the children to work on photocopiable page 37 (the quiz).

REVIEW

■ Go through the answers to the quiz.

■ Try to ensure everyone understands the key facts by the end of the lesson.

■ If you have time, the following is a perfect demonstration of how water travels through a plant. Take a stick of celery and cut it in half lengthways. Place the celery in a jar of water coloured with food colouring. After a few hours the coloured water can clearly be seen in the stem.

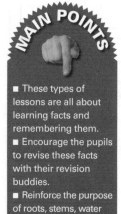

■ These types of lessons are all about learning facts and remembering them.
■ Encourage the pupils to revise these facts with their revision buddies.
■ Reinforce the purpose of roots, stems, water and leaves.

■ The children could conduct the celery experiment (see 'Don't Panic!' above) at home using either celery or a white flower such as a carnation (the colour will appear in the petals).

Plant-growth quiz

1. What do all plants and living things need?

2. Name two things a plant takes from the soil.

3. What keeps a plant firmly anchored?

4. What is the job of a plant's stem?

5. What is the purpose of a plant's leaves? (Tick only one box.)

☐ **a.** To provide food for insects

☐ **b.** To make food for the plant

☐ **c.** To provide shelter for insects from predators

6. What do leaves try to trap? (Tick only one box.)

☐ **a.** Small insects

☐ **b.** Large mammals

☐ **c.** Sunlight

7. Why would a gardener add fertiliser to water in a watering can when she or he was watering a plant in a pot?

LESSON OBJECTIVE
Sc2: Green plants –
Reproduction
2d. Pupils should be
taught the parts of a
flower and their role in
the life cycle of
flowering plants,
including pollination,
seed formation, seed
dispersal and
germination.

WHAT YOU NEED
■ Photocopiable page
39 'Parts of a flower
and seed dispersal'
■ Writing materials
■ Flowers (optional)

PARTS OF A FLOWER AND SEED DISPERSAL

INTRODUCTION

■ Recap the last lesson on plant growth.

■ Explain that this lesson also involves learning
scientific facts; on this occasion about how
plants reproduce. If they can remember these
facts and explain these processes they will be
working at Level 4.

WHOLE CLASS TEACHING

■ Write these key facts about flower parts on the
board and go over the definitions of each one:

■ Ovary: the seed 'box'

■ Ovule: the undeveloped seed

■ Petal: the colourful outer part of the flower

■ Stamen: the male part of the flower that
produces pollen

■ Stigma: the top of the female part of the flower

■ Anther: the end of the stamen in which the
pollen can be found

■ Explain the life cycle of flowering parts:

Pollination ⟶ seed formation ⟶ seed
dispersal ⟶ germination

■ Hand out photocopiable page 39 and organise
the children into groups.

■ Ask the groups to work through section A of the
sheet, discussing the various parts and labelling
them accordingly.

■ Talk about the different methods of seed
dispersal: birds/animals, wind, water.

■ Children can then complete section B as an
independent exercise.

REVIEW

■ Ensure the entire class have labelled the parts of
a flower correctly.

■ Go over the correct answers to section B.

■ Learn the parts of a
flower and label them
on a diagram.
■ Learn the life cycle of
a flowering plant.
■ Learn the different
methods of seed
dispersal.

■ A useful memory
tool for remembering
the male and female
parts of a flower.
StaMEN = male
StigMA (as in mum!) =
female

■ Practise labelling the
parts of a flower with a
revision buddy.
■ At home (or in class
if you have time), open
up a real flower and
identify the parts.

Parts of a flower and seed dispersal

The diagram shows a cross section of a flower.

1. Identify **a** on the diagram.
2. identify **b** on the diagram.

3. Identify **c** on the diagram.
4. Identify **d** on the diagram.
5. Identify **e** on the diagram.
6. Identify **f** on the diagram.

petal
ovary
anther
stigma
stamen
ovule

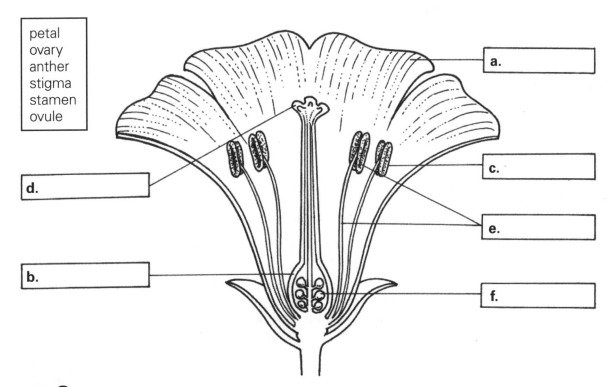

a.

c.

e.

d.

b.

f.

Seed dispersal
Give an example of seeds that are dispersed by each of the following methods:

7. Birds or animals

8. Wind

9. Water

LESSON OBJECTIVE
Sc2: Humans and other animals – Movement 2e. Pupils should be taught that humans and some other animals have skeletons and muscles to support and protect their bodies and to help them move

WHAT YOU NEED
■ Photocopiable page 41, 'The Human skeleton'
■ Writing materials
■ Model skeleton (optional)

THE HUMAN SKELETON

INTRODUCTION

■ Ask the class what we would be like without a skeleton (a blobby mass on the floor).

■ Find out which parts of the skeleton the children know. Aim for the scientific names, not 'leg-bone', etc.

WHOLE CLASS TEACHING

■ If you have a model skeleton, identify the bones that the children have mentioned. If not, hand out photocopiable page 41 and use that instead. You should be able to identify at least the following: skull, ribcage, shoulder blade, femur (thigh bone), patella (knee cap), spine with individual vertebrae, and the pelvis.

■ Label the identified bones on the skeleton diagram on the photocopiable page.

■ Set the children to work on answering the questions on the photocopiable page.

REVIEW

■ Go over the answers to the questions.

■ Ensure that everyone has understood the 'Main points' of the lesson.

■ Some pupils may enquire about unusual bones such as metatarsals, which they will have heard about through the news of footballers and their injuries. Identify these on the model skeleton or diagram.

MAIN POINTS

Humans and some other animals have skeletons to help them:
■ move
■ support their bodies
■ protect vital organs.

DON'T PANIC!

If you do not have a model skeleton, there are some excellent diagrams available on internet encyclopaedias.

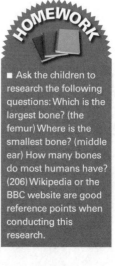

HOMEWORK

■ Ask the children to research the following questions: Which is the largest bone? (the femur) Where is the smallest bone? (middle ear) How many bones do most humans have? (206) Wikipedia or the BBC website are good reference points when conducting this research.

The human skeleton

1. Draw a line from each box to the correct part of the skeleton.

2. Write three reasons why we need our skeletons. _____

_____

_____

_____

This bone is called the pelvis.

This is a hinge joint in the arm.

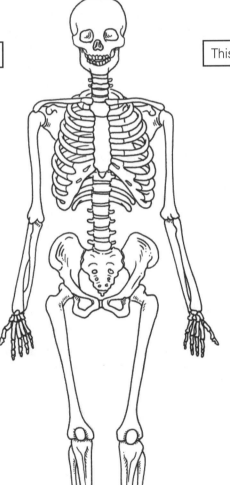

These bones protect the major organs.

These bones protect the brain.

These bones protect important nerves and help you keep upright.

This is a ball and socket joint in the leg.

QUICK FIX FOR YEAR 6: **SCIENCE**

LIVING PROCESSES

LESSON OBJECTIVES

Sc2: Life processes
1. Pupils should be taught that:
a. The life processes common to humans and other animals include nutrition, movement, growth and reproduction
b. The life processes common to plants include growth, nutrition and reproduction

WHAT YOU NEED

■ Toy, doll, robot or action figure; preferably one that can move and make noises – a 'Robo-sapien' toy would be perfect.
■ A school pet, such as a hamster or gerbil
■ Photocopiable page 42, 'Living processes'
■ Writing materials

INTRODUCTION

■ Explain that this is extending Level 3 work up to Level 4.

■ In order to reach Level 4 the children will need to show their understanding of living things.

WHOLE CLASS TEACHING

■ Show the class the pet and the toy. We know which one is alive, but how can we tell? The toy should only be able to move, may 'grow' and may have 'senses'. It certainly cannot feed, reproduce, breathe in one gas and release another or get rid of waste materials. List the characteristics of animals on the board.

All animals:

- feed
- breathe in one gas and give out another
- get rid of waste materials
- have senses
- grow
- move
- reproduce.

■ Now ask the following question: *How do we know that a chestnut tree is alive?*

Plants grow, produce seeds (reproduce) and use sunlight, water and air to make food. They do not breathe in the same way as animals, but they do take in air and give out waste gases through their leaves (including oxygen).

■ Ask the class to work through photocopiable page 43.

REVIEW

■ Go over the answers to the photocopiable page.

■ Ensure everyone is familiar with the key facts about living things.

■ In spite of the lesson objective Sc2: 1b (see opposite) suggesting otherwise, plants do in fact move, even if very slowly. Trees will move their leaves to catch sunlight and flowers will open and close for the same reason and to attract insects. This movement should not be confused with other factors, such as trees swaying in the wind.

■ Learn the facts about animals and plants and their life processes.

■ Revise the key facts about living things with your revision buddy. They could be displayed as a poster or information sheet.

Living processes

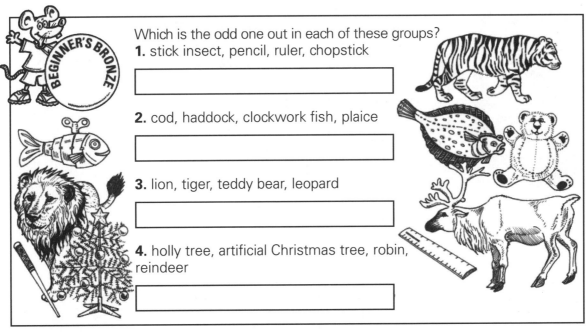

Which is the odd one out in each of these groups?

1. stick insect, pencil, ruler, chopstick

2. cod, haddock, clockwork fish, plaice

3. lion, tiger, teddy bear, leopard

4. holly tree, artificial Christmas tree, robin, reindeer

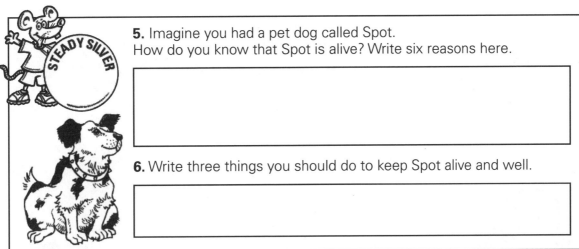

5. Imagine you had a pet dog called Spot.
How do you know that Spot is alive? Write six reasons here.

6. Write three things you should do to keep Spot alive and well.

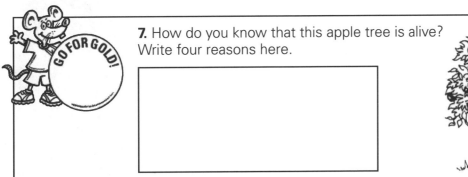

7. How do you know that this apple tree is alive?
Write four reasons here.

LESSON OBJECTIVE

Sc2: Variation and classification
4c. Pupils should be taught that the variety of plants and animals makes it important to identify them and assign them to groups

WHAT YOU NEED

■ Photocopiable page 45, 'Classification'
■ Writing materials
■ Access to the internet and/or library (optional)

CLASSIFICATION

INTRODUCTION

■ Explain that to reach Level 4 the pupils will need to be able to classify organisms. This means putting them into groups with similar characteristics.

WHOLE CLASS TEACHING

■ Ask the class to name different groups of animals. Answers should include: birds, mammals, insects, reptiles and fish.

■ Discuss some of the characteristics of each group: birds have feathers and two legs; mammals are hairy and give birth to live young; insects have six legs and lay eggs; reptiles have scaly skin and are cold-blooded; fish breathe through gills and have scales.

■ This apparently easy task of classifying animals can be deceptive! Tell the class that putting animals into particular groups can be hard, because not all animals fit into the correct mould; they do not all share all the characteristics of their group. Some examples include:

■ whales and dolphins are mammals but do not have hair

■ sharks are fish, but give birth to live young

■ snakes have scaly skin, but do not have legs

■ spiders have eight legs – they are not insects, they are classed as arachnids

■ the duck-billed platypus is an egg-laying mammal!

■ Set the class to work on photocopiable page 45.

MAIN POINTS

■ Learn the main characteristics for each group of animals.
■ Remember, there can be exceptions, or rather a particular animal may not seem to fit a group if the criteria are limited. If this is the case, does it fulfil other criteria?
■ Plants are classified as well as animals.

REVIEW

■ Go over the answers to the photocopiable page.

■ Discuss any unusual animals that the class may bring up. Encourage the children to give reasons for their classifications. For example: *A penguin is a bird because it has feathers, two feet and lays eggs.*

■ You should be able to classify any animal by conducting a thorough search on the internet.

HOMEWORK

■ The children could practise classifying animals with their revision buddy using the internet and reference books. Start with easy ones and then ask other questions such as: Is a squid a fish?

Classification

Add these animals to the correct groups.

1. dog, hawk, trout, crocodile, ant

dog

hawk

trout

crocodile

ant

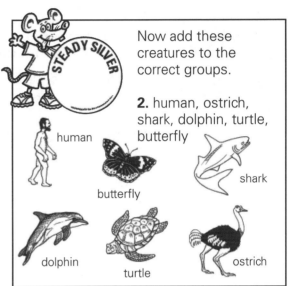

Now add these creatures to the correct groups.

2. human, ostrich, shark, dolphin, turtle, butterfly

human

butterfly

shark

dolphin

turtle

ostrich

mammal	**bird**	**fish**

reptile	**insect**	**none of these**

These may be a little harder, but try placing them in the correct group.

3. fruit bat, spider, octopus, penguin, komodo dragon

spider

fruit bat

octopus

penguin

komodo dragon

LESSON OBJECTIVE
Sc2: Variation and classification
4a. Pupils should be taught how to make and use keys

WHAT YOU NEED
■ Photocopiable page 47, 'Keys'
■ Writing materials

KEYS

INTRODUCTION

■ Explain that using keys can help to classify animals and plants more accurately.

■ If you can read and use a key then you are working at a Level 4.

WHOLE CLASS TEACHING

■ Write this question on the board:

DON'T PANIC!

■ Following a classification key is like the use of flow charts in basic computer programming. You could investigate writing a simple computer program to assist with classifying plants and animals. Something to think about after SATs!

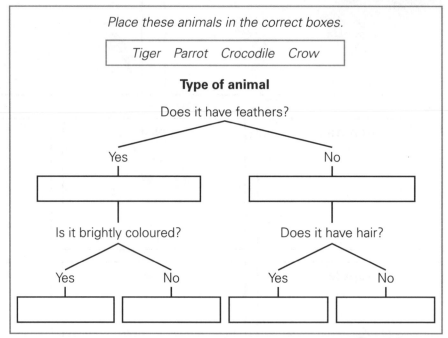

Place these animals in the correct boxes.

| Tiger   Parrot   Crocodile   Crow |

Type of animal

Does it have feathers?

Yes — No

Is it brightly coloured? — Does it have hair?

Yes   No — Yes   No

■ Work through the question with the class as a group activity.

■ Hand out copies of photocopiable page 47 and ask the pupils to complete the activities.

REVIEW

■ Go over the questions on the photocopiable page.

■ Ask the group to suggest other animals that could fit into the boxes of the example on the board.

HOMEWORK

■ Work with your revision buddy playing 'What am I?' One of you chooses an animal; the other has to guess what you are. The person who is the animal can only answer 'yes' or 'no'. Swap over. The person who identifies the other person's animal in the fewest guesses is the winner.

MAIN POINTS

■ Think clearly and read the question at least twice.
■ Check your answers – do they make sense?
■ Think logically and work systematically.

Keys

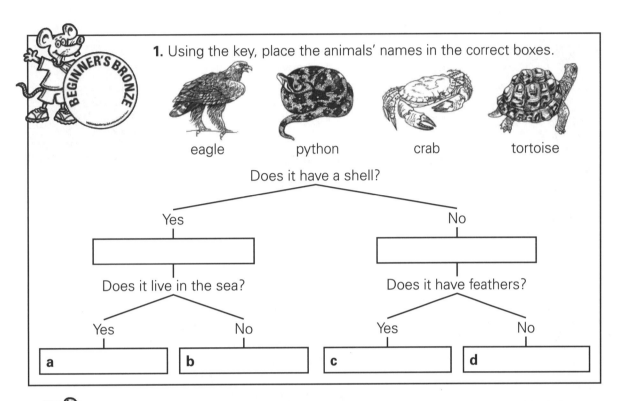

1. Using the key, place the animals' names in the correct boxes.

eagle   python   crab   tortoise

Does it have a shell?

Yes   No

Does it live in the sea?   Does it have feathers?

Yes   No   Yes   No

a   **b**   **c**   **d**

---

2. Name two other animals that could be placed in each of the boxes:

a =

b =

c =

d =

---

3. Which group do each of these animals belong to?
Use a book or the internet if you need help.

a eagle

b python

c crab

d tortoise

ADAPTATION

LESSON OBJECTIVES

Sc2: Living things in their environment – Feeding relationships
5. Pupils should be taught:
b. About the different plants and animals found in different habitats
c. How animals and plants in two different habitats are suited to their environment

WHAT YOU NEED

■ Photocopiable page 49, 'Adaptation'
■ Writing materials

INTRODUCTION

■ Animals and plants need to adapt successfully to the place they live – their environment or 'habitat' – in order to survive. In order for you to survive the National Tests and reach Level 4 you need to know how they do that!

WHOLE CLASS TEACHING

■ Ask the class to think of some wild animals – five or six from different classifications.

■ Discuss where each of these animals lives (its habitat).

■ Discuss what attributes these animals have that enable them to be a success in that habitat.

■ Discuss what would happen if the animal was moved to a different habitat – to the animal itself and to the other animals in that habitat. (e.g. Poisonous cane toads were introduced to Australia from South America in the 1930s to control a beetle population that was destroying sugar crops. There are now millions of cane toads and they have proved fatal to Australian flora and fauna and delicate ecosystems.)

■ Have the children complete photocopiable page 49 on adaptation.

REVIEW

■ Go over the correct answers to the questions on photocopiable page.

■ Discuss any issues that might have arisen from the photocopiable page.

■ The place where an animal or plant lives is called a 'habitat'.
■ Think about different adaptations and how they help animals and plants to survive. For example, an antelope has long legs to escape predators and also horns to defend it if caught; a cactus has deep roots to reach water in the desert.
■ If animals are unable to adapt to their habitats they will be on course for extinction. For example, extensive deforestation in Sumatra and Borneo has led to an 80 percent decrease in the orang-utan population over the last 20 years. The lowland forests in which they thrive have been decimated.

■ If he has not been studied before (in the 'Finding out' lesson), the children could do some internet research on Charles Darwin and his theory of evolution. They could then produce an information sheet on his work and its importance today.

Adaptation

1. Draw a line from each animal to its habitat and then a line to the adaptation that helps it survive there.

Animal	Habitat	Adaptation
tiger	desert	streamlined body to swim fast
dolphin	Antarctic	stripes for camouflage when hunting
penguin	sea	long beak to catch fish
camel	jungle	thick coat of feathers to keep warm
heron	fast-flowing river	strong tail to swim upstream
salmon	riverbank	conserves food and water and goes for long periods without eating

2. Suggest three ways in which a polar bear has adapted to living in the Arctic.

3. Cacti are found in deserts and dry areas. They have adapted to their environment and survive very well in harsh conditions. Explain how these adaptations help the cactus succeed.

a. Deep roots

b. Sharp, spiny covering

c. Tough, thick stems

LESSON OBJECTIVE
Sc2: Living things in their environment – Feeding relationships 5d. Pupils should be taught to use food chains to show feeding relationships in a habitat

WHAT YOU NEED
■ Photocopiable page 51, 'Predators and their prey'
■ Writing materials

PREDATORS AND THEIR PREY

INTRODUCTION

■ Write this definition of the word 'predator' on the board: 'An animal that hunts, kills and eats other animals.'

■ Write this definition of 'prey' on the board: 'An animal that is hunted and killed for food by another animal.'

WHOLE CLASS TEACHING

■ Ask the class for an example of a predator and the prey that it eats.

■ Write up some examples on the board. Can the class make a chain beyond two animals - the predator and the prey? For example, the seal eats the large fish, but the white shark eats the seal and the large fish eats smaller fish, which eat…

■ Work through photocopiable page 51 as a group.

REVIEW

■ Go over the answers on the photocopiable page.

■ Discuss any questions that might have arisen from what the children should find an interesting subject.

DON'T PANIC!

■ Ask the class whether they would prefer to be prey or predator. Most will probably answer that they would rather be a predator! However, you could point out that both roles have advantages and disadvantages. If you were a top predator like a lion, you would be fine as long as you were fit and healthy. If you sustained an injury on a hunt that incapacitated you, you would starve to death. On the other hand, animals such as wildebeest, which lions hunt, use safety in numbers for protection as well as their formidable horns. It is usually only the old and weak (the young) that fall victim to the lion.

MAIN POINTS
■ 'Prey' is eaten by other animals.
■ 'Predators' eat other animals.
■ The arrows are always drawn towards the predator.

HOMEWORK
■ Research the phrase 'top predator' and name three examples.

Predators and their prey

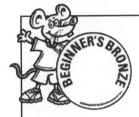

1. Draw an arrow from each prey to its predator.

prey

predator

2. Look at these food chains:
a. seaweed ➝ shrimp ➝ haddock
b. leaves ➝ caterpillar ➝ thrush
c. grass ➝ zebra ➝ lion

What type of plant do all these food chains begin with?

3. What else is needed to start virtually every food chain?

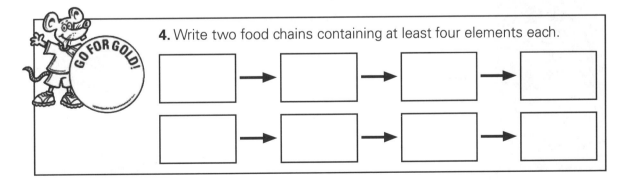

4. Write two food chains containing at least four elements each.

FOOD CHAINS

LESSON OBJECTIVE
Sc2: Living things in their environment – Feeding relationships 5e. Pupils should be taught how nearly all food chains start with a green plant

WHAT YOU NEED
■ Photocopiable page 53, 'Food chains'
■ Writing materials

INTRODUCTION

■ Explain that this lesson is building on work touched on in the previous lesson.

WHOLE CLASS TEACHING

■ Ask the class what every food chain starts with. They should reply 'the sun'. Explain that the sun is essential for all life; without it there would be no life on earth at all.

■ Now ask the class what nearly every food chain begins with. If they were paying attention in the last lesson they should answer 'a green plant'.

■ Discuss the food stuffs that humans consume. Keep it relevant to the class; what animal-based food stuffs do their parents or carers buy at the supermarket?

■ Aim for a list containing items such as sausages, chicken, roast beef, etc.

■ Draw on the board a food chain for each one. For example:

Sun ⟶ grass ⟶ cow ⟶ human

Sun ⟶ grain ⟶ chicken ⟶ human

■ Do the same for non-animal based food stuffs, for example, apple juice:

Sun ⟶ apple tree ⟶ apple juice ⟶ human

■ Discuss food chains in the animal kingdom. Write an example on the board:

Sun ⟶ algae ⟶ shrimp ⟶ small fish ⟶ large fish ⟶ seal ⟶ killer whale

■ Hand out copies of photocopiable page 53 and ask them to start work.

REVIEW

■ Go over the answers to the questions on the photocopiable page.

■ Discuss any points that might have arisen.

DON'T PANIC!

■ When dealing with food stuffs like cheese or eggs, it does not matter if we do not actually eat the animal itself. The food chain should be drawn as if we did. So, the egg food chain would be the same as the chicken food chain and the cheese food chain the same as the cow food chain.

MAIN POINTS

■ The sun is essential for life on earth.
■ Nearly all food chains begin with a green plant.
■ Humans are the top predator on the planet although some humans experience animal attacks (sharks, crocodiles, tigers, etc.).

HOMEWORK

■ Can you find a food chain that does not begin with a green plant? (Some bacteria in deep sea vents break down inorganic material to gain their energy.)

Food chains

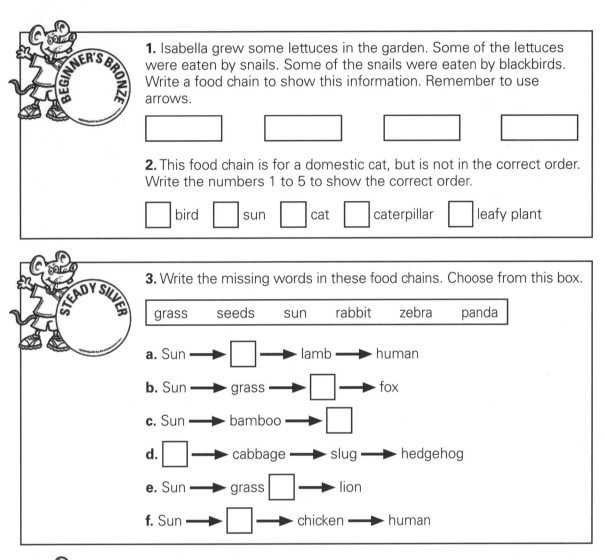

1. Isabella grew some lettuces in the garden. Some of the lettuces were eaten by snails. Some of the snails were eaten by blackbirds. Write a food chain to show this information. Remember to use arrows.

2. This food chain is for a domestic cat, but is not in the correct order. Write the numbers 1 to 5 to show the correct order.

☐ bird   ☐ sun   ☐ cat   ☐ caterpillar   ☐ leafy plant

3. Write the missing words in these food chains. Choose from this box.

grass   seeds   sun   rabbit   zebra   panda

a. Sun ⟶ ☐ ⟶ lamb ⟶ human

b. Sun ⟶ grass ⟶ ☐ ⟶ fox

c. Sun ⟶ bamboo ⟶ ☐

d. ☐ ⟶ cabbage ⟶ slug ⟶ hedgehog

e. Sun ⟶ grass ☐ ⟶ lion

f. Sun ⟶ ☐ ⟶ chicken ⟶ human

4. Here is a list of words which form a food chain that exists off the coast of California.

sun   animal plankton   great white shark   plant plankton
large fish   small shrimp   seal   small fish

Write the Californian food chain in the correct order.

MICRO-ORGANISMS

LESSON OBJECTIVE

Sc2: Living things in their environment – Micro-organisms 5f. Pupils should be taught that micro-organisms are living organisms that are often too small to be seen, and that they may be beneficial or harmful.

WHAT YOU NEED

■ Photocopiable page 55, 'Micro-organisms'
■ Writing materials
■ A microscope and samples of micro-organisms such as fungi (optional)
■ An apple (or a piece of fruit)

INTRODUCTION

■ Explain that micro-organisms can only be seen using a microscope.

■ If you have a microscope and a sample, then allow the group to view it.

WHOLE CLASS TEACHING

■ Explain that we are surrounded by micro-organisms such as bacteria, viruses and fungi. Some of these are helpful to us and some are not.

■ Some bacteria, viruses and fungi can make us ill. Ask the class to come up with a list of illnesses!

■ Bacterial illnesses include: salmonella (a form of food poisoning), tetanus, cholera, dysentery and diarrhoea. Antibiotics can treat infections caused by bacteria.

■ Viral illnesses include: the common cold, influenza, measles, chicken pox, rabies, herpes, HIV, polio and mumps. Vaccinations can help people become immune to some viral diseases but not all.

■ Fungal illnesses include: ringworm and athlete's foot.

■ Other bacteria and fungi are useful. For example, our gut contains billions of bacteria which break down our food into waste and extract the goodness from the rest. Other bacteria in our intestines stop harmful microbes growing and making us ill.

■ Useful fungi include yeast. Yeast is used in bread making, brewing beer and making wine.

■ Hand out photocopiable page 55 and ask the pupils to start work.

REVIEW

■ Go over the questions on the sheet and reinforce the 'Main points' of the lesson.

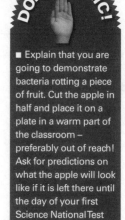

■ Explain that you are going to demonstrate bacteria rotting a piece of fruit. Cut the apple in half and place it on a plate in a warm part of the classroom – preferably out of reach! Ask for predictions on what the apple will look like if it is left there until the day of your first Science National Test paper – an on-going experiment! (Make sure the cleaner is aware of the experiment too.)

■ Some micro-organisms can be useful and some harmful to humans.
■ Viruses cannot be treated by antibiotics, but you can be immunised by vaccination.
■ Yeast (a fungus) and bacteria are used in food production such as yoghurt and cheese.

■ The children could research Edward Jenner and his work on vaccination, using the library or the internet. (Two pages of questions about Jenner and scientific enquiry, worth six marks, appeared in the 2003 National Tests paper.)

Micro-organisms

Tick true or false after these statements.

True **False**

1. All micro-organisms are harmful and should be killed with disinfectant. ☐ ☐

2. Viruses are useful for making bread. ☐ ☐

3. The common cold is a virus. ☐ ☐

4. The common cold can be cured by antibiotics. ☐ ☐

5. Ringworm is a small worm which burrows into your flesh and slowly eats you alive. ☐ ☐

6. Children and adults in the UK are given vaccinations so they become immune to many viruses. ☐ ☐

7. Draw three types of food stuff which are made using micro-organisms.

8. List three jobs bacteria perform in the human gut.

_____

_____

_____

LESSON OBJECTIVE

Sc3: Grouping and classifying materials 1b Pupils should be taught that some materials are better thermal insulators than others

WHAT YOU NEED

■ Photocopiable page 57 'Thermal insulators and conductors'
■ Writing materials

THERMAL INSULATORS AND CONDUCTORS

INTRODUCTION

■ Explain that the children are expected to know that heat travels more easily through some materials than others.

■ Write on the board these definitions of thermal insulators and conductors:

  ■ Thermal insulator: 'A material that reduces or stops the transmission of heat.'

  ■ Thermal conductor: 'A material that allows the transmission of heat.'

WHOLE CLASS TEACHING

■ Ask the class to suggest materials that would make good thermal insulators and conductors. List their suggestions on the board.

■ Ask the class where and when good thermal insulators and conductors would be useful. List their suggestions on the board.

■ Discuss the responses.

■ Hand out copies of photocopiable page 57 and set the children to work in groups.

REVIEW

■ Establish that all the children have understood the main points of the lesson.

■ Go over any words or sentences in the cloze exercise on page 57 that caused problems.

MAIN POINTS

■ Metals are excellent conductors of heat. Heat can travel through them very easily.
■ China and pottery (teacups, for example) are fairly good conductors of heat.
■ Wood, plastic and polystyrene are poor conductors of heat – they are insulators.

DON'T PANIC!

■ The children should already know which materials conduct electricity and which do not. (All metals do, most non-metals are electrical insulators.) Think of thermal conductors in the same way. A conductor of electricity lets electricity through; a conductor of heat lets heat pass through.

HOMEWORK

■ Find three examples of good thermal insulators and conductors around the home. Present your findings as a poster.

Thermal insulators and conductors

Choose a word from this box to fill in the gaps in the paragraphs below.

copper	electricity	easily	cooker	gloves	hot	materials
polystyrene	china	metal	investigation	bare	insulator	

_____ wire is used to conduct _____ because it allows the electricity to pass through it very _____ . Likewise, aluminium is used to make saucepans because the heat from the _____ travels easily through to the contents of the saucepan. We use oven _____ to take hot dishes out of the oven because the thick material used to make the gloves is an excellent insulator. A tea cosy on a teapot is a useful insulator as it helps keep the tea _____ for longer. If we know which _____ make good thermal insulators and conductors, we can use the knowledge to good effect.

Ruby filled three cups with hot water. One of the cups was metal, one was polystyrene and one was made of china. Which one do you think kept the water hot for the longest time? The correct answer is the _____ one, followed by the _____ one and then the _____ one.

Ruby then conducted an _____ with two ice cubes. She held one in the bare palm of her hand and the other one in a gloved hand. Which one melted first? The ice cube in the _____ hand melted first. The glove acted as a good _____ .

Complete these sentences:

1. Metal is the best material for a radiator because it is a good...

2. Plastic is not used to make radiators because it is a good...

LESSON OBJECTIVE

Sc3: Grouping and classifying materials 1e. Pupils should be taught to recognise differences between solids, liquids and gases, in terms of ease of flow and maintenance of shape and volume

WHAT YOU NEED

■ Photocopiable page 59 'Gases'
■ Writing materials
■ A glass of sparkling water or can of fizzy drink

SOLIDS, LIQUIDS AND GASES

INTRODUCTION

■ Explain to the class that in order to achieve Level 4, they need to know the names of different gases and understand that materials can be solid, liquid or gas.

WHOLE CLASS TEACHING

■ Ask the class to name as many gases as they can and to write them on the board. You should have a list containing at least the following: oxygen, carbon dioxide, hydrogen, helium and nitrogen.

■ Explain that water vapour is a gas and that 'air' is a mixture of gases that includes mainly nitrogen, oxygen, water vapour and carbon dioxide.

■ Show the class the can of fizzy drink or the glass of fizzy water. Identify the solid (aluminium or glass), the liquid (drink/water) and gas (carbon dioxide bubbles).

■ Set the class to work on photocopiable page 59.

REVIEW

■ Go over the answers to the questions on the photocopiable page.

■ Name a number of different materials and ask the class to decide whether they are solid, liquid or gas. Include tricky ones like shampoo and ketchup (liquids) or marshmallows (solid).

DON'T PANIC!

■ Some solids, liquids and gases can change from one state to another. Water can freeze and become solid; chocolate can melt and become a liquid. Some of these changes are reversible (ice can melt back to liquid); others are not (the wax burnt from a candle – not to be confused with drips of melted wax).

MAIN POINTS

■ Solids keep their shape unless they are squashed or moved and can be cut into pieces.
■ Liquids flow and assume the shape of the container or surface that holds them.
■ Gases flow in all directions and spread out to fill the space they are in.

HOMEWORK

■ Using books and the internet, investigate the behaviour and structure of solid, liquid and gas particles.

Solids, liquids and gases

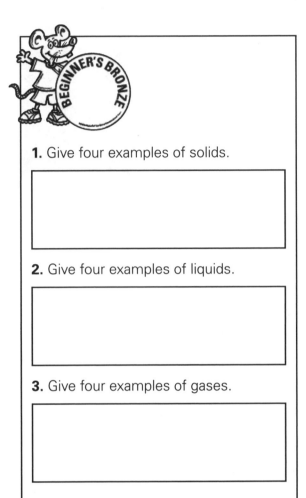

BEGINNER'S BRONZE

1. Give four examples of solids.

2. Give four examples of liquids.

3. Give four examples of gases.

STEADY SILVER

4. Describe the properties of a solid.

_____

_____

_____

5. Describe the properties of a liquid.

_____

_____

_____

6. Describe the properties of a gas.

_____

_____

_____

_____

GO FOR GOLD!

7. Write the name of each of these materials in the correct column.

| oxygen   milk   helium   rock   cooking oil   butter chocolate   syrup   nitrogen |

Solids at room temperature	Liquids at room temperature	Gases at room temperature

LESSON OBJECTIVE
Sc3: Grouping and classifying materials 1a. Pupils should be taught to compare everyday materials and objects on the basis of their material properties, including hardness, strength, flexibility and magnetic behaviour, and to relate these properties to everyday uses of the materials

WHAT YOU NEED
- Photocopiable page 60, 'Grouping and classifying materials'
- Writing materials

GROUPING AND CLASSIFYING MATERIALS

INTRODUCTION

- Explain that the children will need to be able to classify materials.

- Highlight the links to the earlier lessons on classifying animals (page 44) and using keys (page 46).

■ Think about the properties of materials when you classify them, such as hardness/softness, strength/weakness, flexibility/rigidity, solid, liquid, gas, alive at some point/inanimate.

WHOLE CLASS TEACHING

- Remind the class about classifying animals and using a key.

- Work through this question on the board:

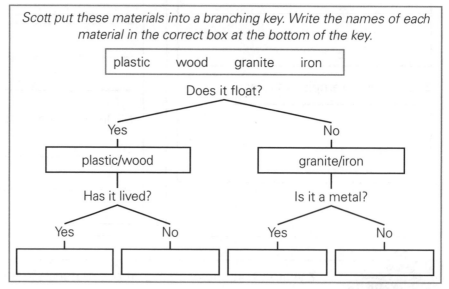

Scott put these materials into a branching key. Write the names of each material in the correct box at the bottom of the key.

| plastic | wood | granite | iron |

Does it float?

Yes — plastic/wood

No — granite/iron

Has it lived? Yes / No

Is it a metal? Yes / No

- Set the class to work on photocopiable page 61.

REVIEW

- Work through the questions on the photocopiable page as a group. Stress the importance of answering each question correctly. These classification questions offer the opportunity for 'easy marks' in the National Tests.

■ Read the questions carefully and think about them in a systematic way.
■ Questions like these often come up in National Test papers so make sure you understand how to answer them.
■ Remember: you should be able to classify anything around you and beyond, including animals and plants.

■ The concept should be ingrained. If not, then redo the activity until it is! Otherwise concentrate any homework time on other areas that need addressing – or give yourself a well-earned break!

Grouping and classifying materials

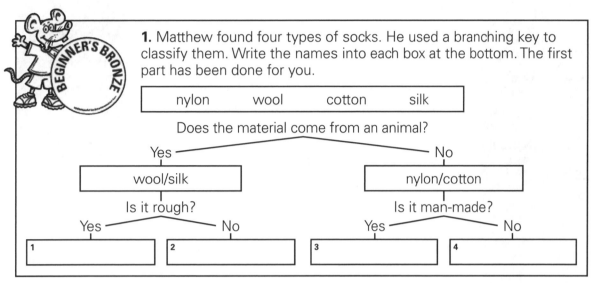

1. Matthew found four types of socks. He used a branching key to classify them. Write the names into each box at the bottom. The first part has been done for you.

| nylon   wool   cotton   silk |

Does the material come from an animal?

Yes — No

| wool/silk | | nylon/cotton |

Is it rough?   Is it man-made?

Yes — No   Yes — No

| 1 | | 2 | | 3 | | 4 |

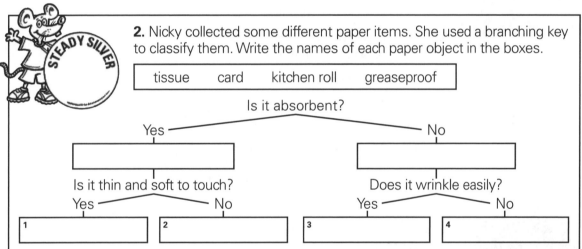

2. Nicky collected some different paper items. She used a branching key to classify them. Write the names of each paper object in the boxes.

| tissue   card   kitchen roll   greaseproof |

Is it absorbent?

Yes — No

Is it thin and soft to touch?   Does it wrinkle easily?

Yes — No   Yes — No

| 1 | | 2 | | 3 | | 4 |

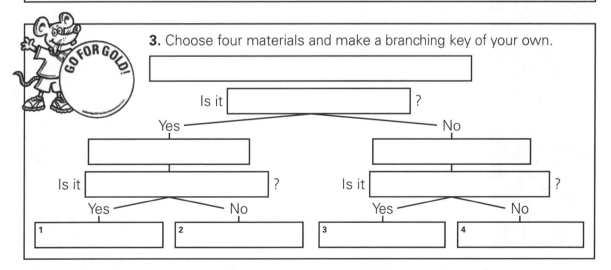

3. Choose four materials and make a branching key of your own.

Is it _____ ?

Yes — No

Is it _____ ?   Is it _____ ?

Yes — No   Yes — No

| 1 | | 2 | | 3 | | 4 |

■SCHOLASTIC
www.scholastic.co.uk

QUICK FIX FOR YEAR 6: SCIENCE

LESSON OBJECTIVES

Sc3: Separating mixtures of materials
3. Pupils should be taught:
a. how to separate solid particles of different sizes by sieving
c. how to separate insoluble solids from liquids by filtering
d. how to recover dissolved solids by evaporating the liquid from the solution

WHAT YOU NEED

■ Photocopiable page 63 'Separating mixtures'
■ Writing materials
■ A jar containing salt, water, sand, marbles, iron filings and woodchips (optional)

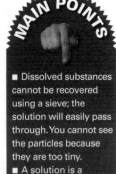

■ Dissolved substances cannot be recovered using a sieve; the solution will easily pass through. You cannot see the particles because they are too tiny.
■ A solution is a mixture where a solid has dissolved.
■ Evaporation happens when a liquid turns to a gas. This will leave behind any solid that was dissolved. in the liquid

SEPARATING MIXTURES

INTRODUCTION

■ To reach Level 4 you will need to know how to separate simple mixtures.

■ There are a number of techniques you can use, depending on the contents of the mixture. You need to decide which techniques to use and in what order.

WHOLE CLASS TEACHING

■ Explain that if the children have time, they could prepare the jar with the contents as listed. If not, draw a diagram with labels, on the board.

■ Explain that this could be completed as a proper investigation using magnets and sieves, etc., but for the purposes of a booster class, the pupils will be covering the objectives in theory only.

■ Ask the class how they would separate the different substances in the jar.

■ Discuss the responses. You are aiming for the following:
a. Use a fine sieve to remove the solid materials.
b. Allow the water to evaporate from the remaining salt solution. (Explain that you could recover the water by boiling the solution and then condensing the water vapour but this would be difficult and quite dangerous to do in the classroom!) The salt will remain and can be recovered.
c. Use a large sieve (or your hands) to pick out the marbles.
d. Use a magnet to remove the iron filings.
e. Mix the remaining sand and woodchips with water and allow the sand to settle (sedimentation). The woodchips will float and can be recovered.
f. Sieve the remaining water and sand and allow the recovered sand to dry.

■ Set the class to work on photocopiable page 63.

REVIEW

■ Go over the activity and address any questions or misconceptions.

■ Ensure the main points have been understood.

■ Sieving is used to separate most undissolved solids from a liquid or to separate two solids of different sizes. Filtering is used to separate a solution from undissolved solids.

■ Try the experiment with the jar and contents at home. Make sure you can correctly spell and explain evaporation, separation, sieving, sedimentation, condensation and filtration.

Separating mixtures

Choose a word from the box to complete each of these sentences.

sieve	filter	magnet	evaporate

Josh wanted to separate some mixtures.

1. He used a _____ to separate iron filings from sand.

2. He used a _____ to separate sand from water.

3. By allowing the water to _____ Josh could separate the salt water solution.

4. To remove gravel from soil, Josh used a _____ .

5. Josh has a jar filled with a mixture of sand, salt and sawdust.
Write three steps for Josh to separate the mixture.

a. _____

_____

_____

b. _____

_____

_____

c. _____

_____

_____

6. Josh has another jar containing the following mixture – sugar, gravel and sand. How can he separate this mixture in three stages?

a. _____

_____

_____

b. _____

_____

_____

c. _____

_____

_____

MAKING SOLUTIONS

INTRODUCTION

■ Explain that the children will need to be able to explain the changes that occur when materials are mixed.

■ To reach Level 4 and beyond the children need to suggest ways in which solids can be made to dissolve faster.

WHOLE CLASS TEACHING

■ Ask the class what a 'solution' is. (Other than 'the answer to a problem!')

■ Inform them that in scientific terms a solution is a 'liquid into which a solid has been mixed and dissolved'.

■ Stress the importance of learning to spell scientific words. Marks can be lost in the National Tests for incorrect spelling of scientific vocabulary.

■ Write on the board: salt, sand, sugar, chalk.

■ Ask the class which of these solids would dissolve in water and what would happen to the ones that did not. (Sugar and salt would dissolve; sand and chalk would sink to the bottom.)

■ Ask how the dissolving process could be speeded up; think of situations where salt and sugar are used at home. (Stirring and heating – cups of tea and using salt in cooking.)

■ Set the class to work on photocopiable page 65.

REVIEW

■ Go over the answers to the questions on the photocopiable page and any other questions raised by the lesson.

■ Ensure that the main points of the lesson are understood by the class.

Making solutions

1. Dominique mixed five solids with warm water and stirred each one for a minute.

Tick the boxes of those that dissolved.

Sand ☐   Sugar ☐   Iron filings ☐   Salt ☐   Soil ☐

2. What happened to the three substances which did not dissolve?

3. Dominique mixed a teaspoon of sugar into:
a. 200ml of cold water;
b. 200ml of warm water and stirred it for a minute.

Which dissolved quicker, **a** or **b**? ☐

4. Explain how Dominique could separate the sugar from the water.

5. Dominique's mother mixed sugar and water in a saucepan and heated it to make syrup. What happened to the sugar?

6. She then boiled the mixture to make toffee. What happened to some of the water?

GRAVITY

INTRODUCTION

■ Tell the class that to gain Level 4 they must be able to describe the effects of gravitational pull.

WHOLE CLASS TEACHING

■ If the class have completed the Level 4 test (pages 18–21), then remind them of question 7. (The raindrops falling to Earth.) Recap the answer and illustrate it on the board.

■ If they are doing the test at the end of the booster classes, then draw the following diagram on the board.

■ Ask for a volunteer and ask the following question: 'If the man was holding a weight on a piece of string, how should you draw it on the diagram?'

■ The child may draw the weighted string hanging vertically down. They should, of course, draw it pointing towards the centre of the Earth. Either way, ask the class for an opinion. Do they agree or disagree with the answer on the board?

■ Set the class to work on photocopiable page 67.

REVIEW

■ Establish the main points and go over any questions that may have arisen from the lesson or the photocopiable activity sheet.

■ The gravitational pull of the Moon is what causes tides in the seas and oceans on Earth.

■ Gravity is a force that acts downwards on all objects. It is what makes things fall when they are dropped and stay on the ground.
■ The pull of gravity depends on where you are in the universe! The Moon is a sixth the size of the Earth. If your weight was measured on the Moon you would weigh a sixth of your weight on Earth, because of the weaker force of gravity on the Moon. If you were weighed on Jupiter (many times larger than Earth) you would weigh thousands of tons!
■ It is the gravitional pull of the Sun that keeps all the planets in orbit. It is the gravitational pull of the Earth that keeps the Moon in orbit around the Earth.

■ Ask the class to research the experiments regarding gravity carried out by astronauts on the Moon. True or false: there are golf balls on the Moon?!

Gravity

1. Name two effects the force of gravity has on Earth.

_____

_____

2. Which has the stronger gravitational pull, the Earth, the Moon or the Sun?

_____

3. Draw an arrow to show the force of gravity on this sky-diver.

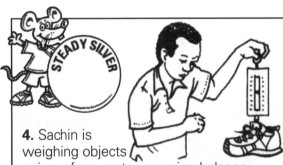

4. Sachin is weighing objects using a forcemeter or spring balance. The objects are weighed in Newtons (N). He records his results in a table:

Object	Weight in Newtons
Training shoe	2.5
Raincoat	14
Bag of apples	6
Empty drink can	0.5

a. Write the items in size order with the heaviest first.

_____

b. What is the name of the force that pulls the objects down?

_____

5. Why do astronauts bounce around on the Moon as if they had springs on their feet?

_____

_____

6. What would happen to us if the Earth suddenly had no gravity?

_____

_____

MAGNETS

INTRODUCTION

■ Explain to the class that in order to reach Level 4 they will need to know about magnetic forces, including which metals are magnetic and which are not.

WHOLE CLASS TEACHING

■ Tell the class that you are going to tell them some important facts about magnets. You will be able to demonstrate these very easily with two magnets that you have provided.

■ Ask if the children know which metals are attracted to magnets. The answer is simple: iron and steel. (Steel is a compound metal that contains iron). All other metals will not be attracted to magnets.

■ Demonstrate this with a magnet and your items.

■ Secondly, magnets have 'poles' – north and south. When you put them together, like poles (for example, north and north) 'repel' and unlike poles 'attract'.

■ Demonstrate this with your two magnets.

■ Set the class to work on photocopiable page 69.

REVIEW

■ Go over the answers to the questions to reinforce the main points of this lesson.

LESSON OBJECTIVE

Sc4: Forces and motion 2a. Pupils should be taught about the forces of attraction and repulsion between magnets, and about the forces of attraction between magnets and magnetic materials.

WHAT YOU NEED

■ Photocopiable page 69, 'Magnets'
■ Writing materials
■ Two magnets and a selection of metallic objects (including iron and steel).

■ If a metal is attracted to a magnet it must contain iron or steel. Some 'tin' cans that attract magnets only have a small amount of tin in them; they are mainly made of steel. The other 'tin' cans are actually made of aluminium.
■ 'Repel' is the proper word for the phrase 'push away'. Make sure you use the term correctly. Likewise, 'attract' is the correct term – do not say 'stick to it'.
■ The 'poles' are the ends of the magnet.

■ The children need to know the main points. Ensure that these are understood by all at the end of the lesson.

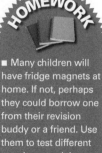

■ Many children will have fridge magnets at home. If not, perhaps they could borrow one from their revision buddy or a friend. Use them to test different metals around the home. Remember, if the magnet attracts the object they are testing, then the metal must contain iron or steel.

Magnets

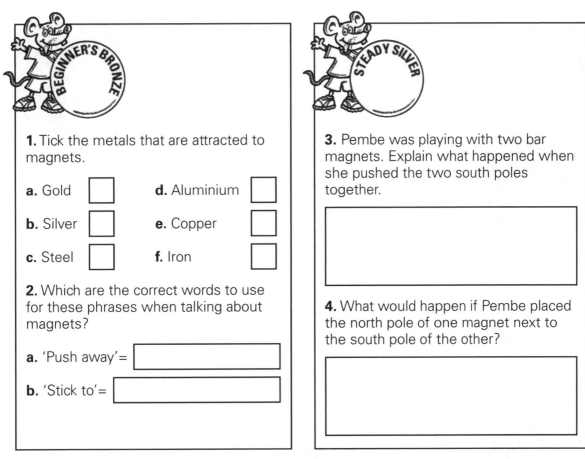

1. Tick the metals that are attracted to magnets.

a. Gold ☐   **d.** Aluminium ☐

b. Silver ☐   **e.** Copper ☐

c. Steel ☐   **f.** Iron ☐

2. Which are the correct words to use for these phrases when talking about magnets?

a. 'Push away' = _____

b. 'Stick to' = _____

3. Pembe was playing with two bar magnets. Explain what happened when she pushed the two south poles together.

4. What would happen if Pembe placed the north pole of one magnet next to the south pole of the other?

5. Draw arrows to show the direction of the force between these north poles.

S   N   N   S

6. Magnetic fields are invisible. Describe one way you would be able to view a magnetic field.

_____

_____

QUICK FIX FOR YEAR 6: SCIENCE

ELECTRICAL CIRCUITS

INTRODUCTION

■ Remind the class that they studied electrical circuits in Key Stage 1.

■ Recap vocabulary such as 'wire', 'battery', 'bulb', 'buzzer' and 'motor'.

■ Ask: *What device can be used to break a circuit?* The class should know it is a switch.

WHOLE CLASS TEACHING

■ Draw these symbols on the board.

Tell the class that circuits are often drawn as diagrams using these symbols.

■ Draw a simple circuit that would light a bulb. Ask the class whether it would light the bulb or not.

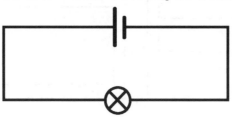

■ Now draw a circuit which would not work because of a break. Discuss with the class and ask them how it could be made to work.

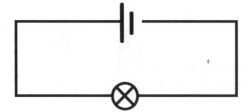

■ Set them to work on photocopiable page 71.

REVIEW

■ The children can swap their activity sheets and check each other's circuit diagrams.

■ Discuss any issues that may arise from the children's diagrams.

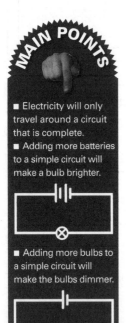

Electrical circuits

1. Max connected a motor to three different circuits. Only one of the motors worked. Tick the correct one.

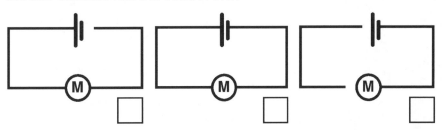

2. Max added switches to his circuits. This time two worked. Tick the correct two.

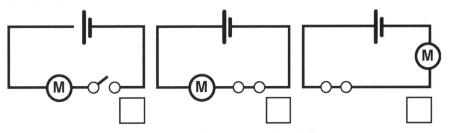

3. Draw a working circuit diagram using at least 3 batteries, 2 bulbs, 1 buzzer, 1 motor and 1 switch, and as much wire as you need.

SUN, EARTH AND MOON

INTRODUCTION

■ Refer back to the lesson on gravity (pages 66–7) and recap the main points. Did anyone find out about the golf balls on the Moon? (In 1971, astronaut Alan Shepherd hit three golf balls on the surface of the Moon. He missed the first two shots, but hit the third and famously reported to Mission Control; 'It's gone for miles and miles and miles!')

WHOLE CLASS TEACHING

■ Explain to the class that you are going to give them some information about the Sun, Earth and Moon and then quiz them on the facts.

■ The Earth orbits the Sun once a year (365¼ days). Ask the class why we have leap years. (To accommodate the ¼ days.)

■ The Moon orbits the Earth roughly every 28 days.

■ The Sun, Earth and Moon are all roughly spherical. Explain that spherical objects are shaped like balls.

■ Day and night are related to the spin of the Earth on its axis. If you have a globe, then use it to show this.

■ Hand out a copy of the quiz (photocopiable page 73). You can allow the children to complete it on their own or in teams. Team play may help less confident learners. You can read it out or let them complete it at their own pace. (You may have to act as question-master for the final question!)

REVIEW

■ Go through the answers to the quiz.

■ The pupils can mark the quizzes and discuss results.

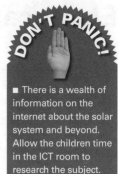
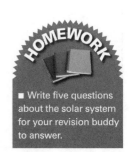

The Sun, Earth and Moon quiz

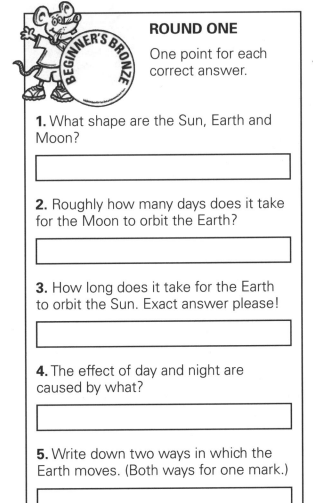

ROUND ONE

BEGINNER'S BRONZE

One point for each correct answer.

1. What shape are the Sun, Earth and Moon?

2. Roughly how many days does it take for the Moon to orbit the Earth?

3. How long does it take for the Earth to orbit the Sun. Exact answer please!

4. The effect of day and night are caused by what?

5. Write down two ways in which the Earth moves. (Both ways for one mark.)

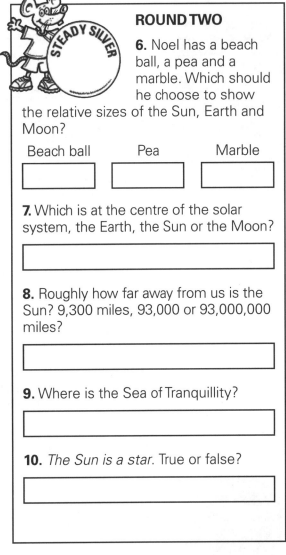

ROUND TWO

STEADY SILVER

6. Noel has a beach ball, a pea and a marble. Which should he choose to show the relative sizes of the Sun, Earth and Moon?

Beach ball   Pea   Marble

7. Which is at the centre of the solar system, the Earth, the Sun or the Moon?

8. Roughly how far away from us is the Sun? 9,300 miles, 93,000 or 93,000,000 miles?

9. Where is the Sea of Tranquillity?

10. *The Sun is a star.* True or false?

ROUND THREE

GO FOR GOLD!

11. In what year did Neil Armstrong and Buzz Aldrin land on the Moon?

12. The Earth tilts at $23\frac{1}{2}$ degrees – one degree either way, and life would not be possible on the planet. True or false?

13. In 1988, what percentage of the population of the USA thought that at least part of the Moon was made of cheese? Closest answer wins the point; exact answer is worth 10 points!

AIR RESISTANCE

INTRODUCTION

■ Explain to the class that to reach Level 4 they have to understand that air resistance is a force that slows down moving objects.

WHOLE CLASS TEACHING

■ Ask the class if they can think of some examples of air resistance and how it slows down moving objects. (The obvious example is a parachute.)

■ Show the class the two pieces of paper – one piece flat and one screwed up. Ask them which one they think will hit the ground first if you drop them at the same time from the same height?

■ Discuss the class responses and demonstrate by completing the investigation.

■ The screwed-up ball will hit the ground first because it has a smaller surface area and so there is less air resistance. The amount of air resistance is affected by the size of the object.

■ Now tear the flat piece of A4 in half and screw it up into a small tight ball. Make the other ball large and loose. Which one will you be able to throw the furthest?

■ Discuss the responses. (You could demonstrate by going into the hall or playground, but it is not essential!)

■ The large loose ball will have more air resistance, so the smaller ball can be thrown the furthest.

■ Set the class to work on photocopiable page 75.

REVIEW

■ Go over the answers to the questions on the photocopiable page and discuss any issues that may have arisen.

■ The children can feel air resistance by waving their hands through the air.

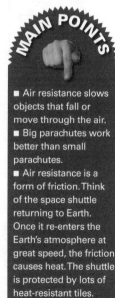

■ Air resistance slows objects that fall or move through the air.
■ Big parachutes work better than small parachutes.
■ Air resistance is a form of friction. Think of the space shuttle returning to Earth. Once it re-enters the Earth's atmosphere at great speed, the friction causes heat. The shuttle is protected by lots of heat-resistant tiles.

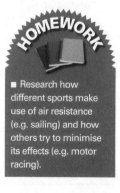

■ Research how different sports make use of air resistance (e.g. sailing) and how others try to minimise its effects (e.g. motor racing).

Air resistance

1. Twins Jack and Jill each weigh 70kg. They jump out of an aeroplane at the same time, each with a parachute made of the same material. Jack's parachute is 25% bigger than Jill's. Who will land on the ground first and why?

_____ will land first because _____

_____

2. Draw arrows to show the air resistance force on Jack and Jill's parachutes.

3. Why do you think aeroplanes have rounded noses? Explain your answer.

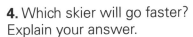

4. Which skier will go faster? Explain your answer.

_____

_____

5. Look at these two lorries. Which one will use less fuel? Why?

_____

_____

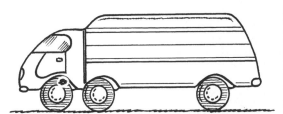

FRICTION

INTRODUCTION

- Remind the class about the previous lesson on air resistance and that air resistance is a form of friction.

- Write on the board the definition of friction, i.e. 'the force that makes it difficult for one object to slide along the surface of another or to move through a liquid or a gas.'

WHOLE CLASS TEACHING

- The children can experience friction by rubbing their hands together; the harder they rub, the more heat is created. (You could refer back to the space shuttle reference in the previous lesson.)

- Ask the class why we wear shoes with grip, (To create as much friction as possible and stop us slipping over.) The opposite of this would be the thin blades of an ice skate, which minimise friction between the skate and the ice, allowing the skater to skate more easily.

- A simple demonstration: place the toy car and eraser at the end of a desk. If I tilt the desk up, which object will move first? The general consensus should be the car! Oblige by tilting the desk; the car will roll down the desk and the eraser should stay where it is. Which has the least friction between it and the desk? (The toy car) Friction prevents the eraser from moving.

- Set the class to work on photocopiable page 77.

REVIEW

- Go over the answers to the photocopiable page and any questions that may arise.

- Ensure everyone is familiar with the main points of the lesson.

LESSON OBJECTIVE
Sc4: Forces and motion 2c. Pupils should be taught about friction, including air resistance, as a force that slows moving objects and may prevent objects from starting to move

WHAT YOU NEED
- Photocopiable page 77, 'Friction'
- Writing materials
- Toy car and an eraser

DON'T PANIC!
- Remember that 'friction' is the name of a type of 'force' and that there are three kinds; surface, air and water.

MAIN POINTS
- Friction is a force. It tries to stop things moving against or through each other.
- Surface friction is when a solid tries to slide against another solid.
- Water resistance is a type of friction and occurs when a solid tries to slide through a liquid (water).
- Air resistance is a type of friction and occurs when a solid tries to move through a gas (air).

HOMEWORK

- With your revision buddy, write three examples in sport where friction is a useful force, and three where we try to reduce friction as much as possible. You could present your work as a poster.

Friction

Add the missing words to these sentences. Choose from the words in the box.

gas	heat	solid	force	liquid	solid

1. Friction is a type of _____ . Surface friction occurs when a _____ tries to slide against another _____ . Air resistance occurs when a solid tries to move through a _____ . Water resistance occurs when a solid tries to move through a _____ . Friction causes _____ .

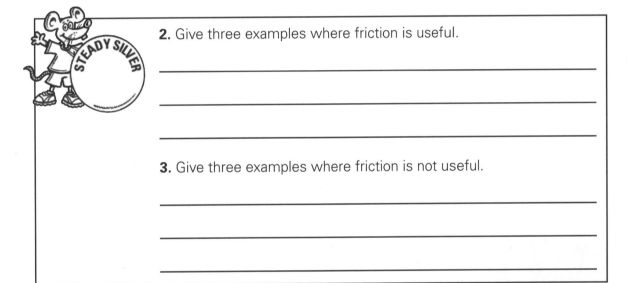

2. Give three examples where friction is useful.

_____

_____

_____

3. Give three examples where friction is not useful.

_____

_____

_____

4. Give a scientific explanation for why rubbing two sticks together can create fire.

_____

_____

5. Give a scientific explanation for why yachts have v-shaped prows.

_____

_____

SOUND

INTRODUCTION

■ Explain that to reach Level 4 the children need to know how sound travels to our ears and to be able to describe how sounds are made when an object vibrates.

WHOLE CLASS TEACHING

■ Explain that vibrating objects create sound. Sometimes this is hard to see, but you can provide your class with a perfect example – something you have probably been telling children to stop doing for years!

■ Twang the ruler on the side of the desk. The sound is caused by the ruler vibrating. This is clearly visible, because it is slow enough to see.

■ If you stop the ruler vibrating, the sound will stop.

■ If you wish, bang a drum with grains of rice on top of it. The vibration (and ensuing sound) can be seen by the rice jumping on the drum-skin.

■ Ask the class: *How does the sound reach our ears?* Discuss their responses. (It travels through the air; it gets fainter the further away you are, because it spreads out.)

■ Set the class to work on photocopiable page 79.

REVIEW

■ Make sure everyone is aware of the main points of this lesson.

■ Go over the answers to the questions on the photocopiable page and discuss any points which may have arisen. The space vacuum/silent world idea will probably cause some debate!

LESSON OBJECTIVES
Sc4: Vibration and sound
3. Pupils should be taught:
e. that sounds are made when objects vibrate but that vibrations are not always directly visible
g. that vibrations from sound sources require a medium through which to travel to the ear.

WHAT YOU NEED
■ Photocopiable page 79, ' Sound'
■ Writing materials
■ A ruler
■ A drum and a few grains of rice (optional)

■ Sound is caused by vibration. The movement of air caused by the vibration creates sound waves.
■ Sound can travel through different materials including air, water, rock and wood.
■ Sound travels through the air to our ears. Anything that stops the sound spreading out will help us to hear it. Think about speaking to your friend down a long tube. You will be able to hear them very clearly.

■ Remember, sound needs something to travel through. We have air in our atmosphere on Earth. Space is a vacuum and so is essentially a silent place. Those explosions in Star Wars should have been very quiet!

■ Make a tin can telephone with your revision buddy.

■ Make sure you know all the facts about sound.

Sound

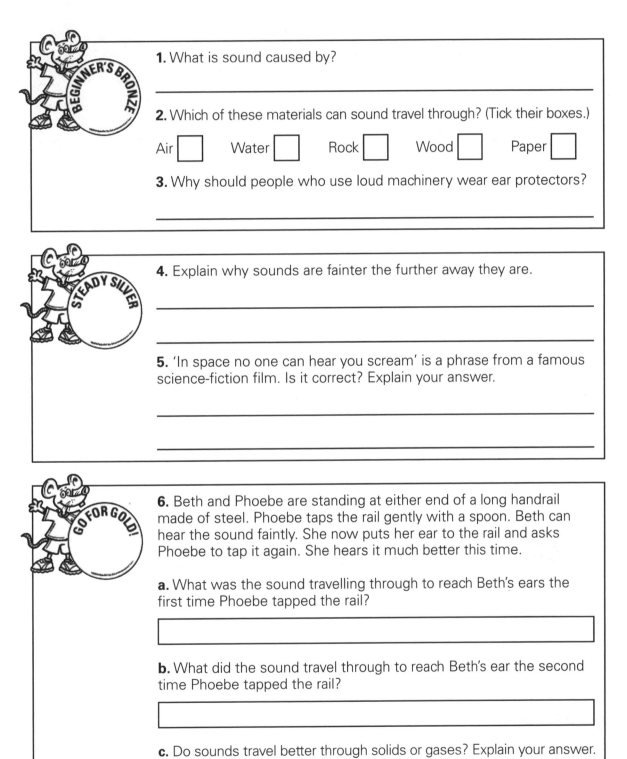

1. What is sound caused by?

_____

2. Which of these materials can sound travel through? (Tick their boxes.)

Air ☐   Water ☐   Rock ☐   Wood ☐   Paper ☐

3. Why should people who use loud machinery wear ear protectors?

_____

4. Explain why sounds are fainter the further away they are.

_____

_____

5. 'In space no one can hear you scream' is a phrase from a famous science-fiction film. Is it correct? Explain your answer.

_____

_____

6. Beth and Phoebe are standing at either end of a long handrail made of steel. Phoebe taps the rail gently with a spoon. Beth can hear the sound faintly. She now puts her ear to the rail and asks Phoebe to tap it again. She hears it much better this time.

a. What was the sound travelling through to reach Beth's ears the first time Phoebe tapped the rail?

☐

b. What did the sound travel through to reach Beth's ear the second time Phoebe tapped the rail?

☐

c. Do sounds travel better through solids or gases? Explain your answer.

☐

LIGHT AND SHADOW

INTRODUCTION

- Explain that there are a number of things that the children need to learn in this final lesson!

WHOLE CLASS TEACHING

- **Fact one:** Light travels from a source. The Sun, fire, and electric lights are light sources. Mirrors, shiny objects and the Moon are not – they reflect light.

- Demonstrate with the torch and mirror.

- **Fact two:** Light cannot pass through some materials; this is how shadows are formed. If an object is opaque, it means it will block light. Transparent means light can pass through.

- Now shine the torch at the book; a dark shadow will be created because the book is opaque. Do the same with the bottle; a faint shadow will be created because most of the light is passing through the bottle. Discuss these observations and explanations with the class.

- Set the class to work on photocopiable page 81.

REVIEW

- Discuss the answers to the questions on the photocopiable page and respond to any questions that arise.

- Congratulate any 100 percent 'attenders' to your booster lessons. Indeed, congratulate the whole class if they have done well!

LESSON OBJECTIVES

Sc4: Light and sound
3. Pupils should be taught:
a. that light travels from a source
b. that light cannot pass through some materials, and how this leads to the formation of shadows
c. that light is reflected from surfaces

WHAT YOU NEED

- Photocopiable page 81, 'Shadows'
- Writing materials
- A torch, a book, a bottle and mirror

- Be careful when talking about solid and opaque objects. There are many solids that are transparent such as some types of glass and plastic.

- Light travels from a source.
- Shadows are formed when light cannot pass through a material. The darkness of a shadow depends on the amount of light let through. (Opaque meaning no light can pass through.)
- Light can be reflected from surfaces.

- With your revision buddy, look through all 30 lessons and worksheets to identify any areas you have problems with. Try and work through these areas together. If between you, you are still unsure of a concept then speak to your teacher. Good luck!

Light and shadow

1. Tick which of these are a source of light.

The Sun ☐   The Moon ☐   A mirror ☐

A burning candle ☐   A lit light bulb ☐   A shiny car ☐

2. Omar is standing in the playground at 10.00am and is casting a shadow. Where does the light come from?

☐

3. Tick one box: Omar is casting a dark shadow because he is:

Tall ☐   Heavy ☐   Smooth ☐

Solid ☐   Opaque ☐   Transparent ☐

4. Shira makes a shadow puppet using her hands and a torch. The shadow appears on the wall. Tick the box beside the correct explanation.

☐ **a.** The shadow forms because Shira's hands are transparent.

☐ **b.** The shadow forms because the light cannot pass through Shira's hands.

☐ **c.** The shadow is a reflection of Shira's hands.

5. The Sun is directly overhead at midday. Are shadows going to be longer or shorter at midday than at 10.00 am?

☐

6. Choose the correct words from the box to complete the sentence.

axis   west   Earth   east

The Sun rises in the _____ and sets in the _____ . It

appears to move across the sky, but it is the _____ spinning on

its _____ which causes this illusion.

SCIENTIFIC ENQUIRY (Sc1)

Success in scientific enquiry is about mastering key skills and conducting experiments in a scientific way. Children should be taught that: **'Science is about thinking creatively to try and explain how living and non-living things work.'**

Here are some useful guidelines to use with pupils, as appropriate:

10 THINGS TO THINK ABOUT WHEN CONDUCTING AN EXPERIMENT:

1. What am I trying to find out?

2. Can I make a prediction?

3. How can I make sure the test is fair?

4. Do I need to change anything?

5. What do I need to keep the same?

6. How shall I record my results?

7. What have I found out?

8. How shall I present my conclusions?

9. Could I test anything else?

10. Can I explain my ideas?

10 TIPS TO STAY SAFE!

1. Follow written instructions carefully.

2. Always listen to your teacher's instructions or questions.

3. Don't be afraid to ask for help if you don't understand an instruction.

4. Let your teacher know if something goes wrong.

5. Be aware of your classmates and what they are doing – they might not be as careful as you!

6. Be extra careful when cutting or heating materials.

7. Do not run in the classroom – you may knock something over and cause an accident.

8. Keep water away from electrical equipment.

9. Wear suitable clothing and goggles if necessary.

10. Always clear up carefully and put things away properly.

10 SKILLS YOU NEED TO REACH LEVEL 4

1. Understand that you need evidence to 'prove' your scientific ideas.

2. Decide on the best way to do an experiment or test.

3. Make predictions about your experiment based on things you have learned.

4. Decide what is the most important information to find out.

5. Choose the most suitable equipment for an experiment.

6. Make scientific observations and be able to explain them.

7. Write down observations and measurements.

8. Draw and understand how to read bar charts.

9. Make conclusions.

10. Suggest ways in which you could do things differently to improve your experiment.

SCIENTIFIC ENQUIRY AND THE NATIONAL TESTS

The National Tests now contain more questions that test their scientific skills as well as pupils' knowledge of scientific facts. The questions are often based on an experiment or description of an investigation that other teachers and children have carried out. Pupils will be presented with the results and findings and be asked to make sense of what has happened in that investigation.

Types of question about experiments and investigations have included:

■ choosing the correct equipment

■ drawing conclusions from a set of results

■ answering questions about graphs, charts and tables

■ completing graphs, charts and tables

■ deciding what question was being investigated

■ describing what had been found out during an investigation.

Pupils may be asked a question about a famous scientist, so it would be worth collating the results from the 'Finding out' lesson (pages 24–25) and creating a class book or folder on the different scientists.

LIFE PROCESSES AND LIVING THINGS (Sc2)

Pupils are taught about the natural world and conduct investigations involving humans, animals and plants. These can be difficult to do in a classroom situation, but this can be addressed by using secondary sources such as the scenarios used in National Test style questions.

To reach Level 4 pupils need to know:

- The basic life processes that humans and other animals share, including how they feed, move, grow and reproduce.

- That the life processes that plants share include growth, nutrition and reproduction.

- That links can be made between life processes in animals and plants and the places where they are found.

- The differences between living and non-living things.

- Animals adapt to their environments in different ways.

- That there are reasons for the adaptations of living things, such as water supply and diet.

- The names and positions of the major organs in the human body.

- The names and positions of some of the organs of a variety of plants.

- How to use simple keys to identify living things.

- How to classify living things.

- How food chains work.

They can develop and extend these skills to reach Level 5.

When conducting investigations with living things or out on field trips, pupils should be encouraged to respect living creatures and the environment. Here are some points to consider with them:

- When working outdoors, wear suitable clothing.

- Take all your litter home with you and dispose of it properly.

- Wash your hands after handling plants and animals.

- Do not eat or drink anything unless your teacher says you may.

- Be particularly careful when around rivers, lakes and the sea. Water is dangerous!

- Do not pick wild flowers or disturb the places where animals live, for example, bird's nests or riverbanks.

MATERIALS AND THEIR PROPERTIES (Sc3)

There are three main topics within this attainment target: grouping and classifying materials, changing materials and separating mixtures of materials.

To reach Level 4 pupils need to:

■ Be able to suggest your own ideas on how to answer a scientific question.

■ Know that evidence is needed to 'prove' scientific ideas and theories.

■ Be able to sort materials into groups on the basis of their properties.

■ Know why some materials are suited to a particular purpose.

■ Know which changes to a material can be reversed.

■ Know which changes to a material cannot be reversed.

■ Know which changes are easy to reverse and which changes are difficult to reverse.

■ Understand the properties of different materials and know how these properties are used in everyday objects.

■ Know how materials are classified into solids, liquids and gases.

■ Know how to separate simple mixtures.

■ Know the meaning (and spelling) of scientific words used to describe changes such as: condense, evaporate, dissolve, melt and freeze.

When doing experiments with materials pupils should be aware of these safety issues:

■ Take extra care when heating or melting materials.

■ Make sure thermometers do not roll off desks.

■ Wash hands after handling soil.

■ Be careful when handling ice – it can 'burn'.

■ Keep long hair tied back when using naked flames.

■ Make sure all spillages are cleaned up quickly and properly.

PHYSICAL PROCESSES (Sc4)

This attainment target has four main areas of study:

- Electricity

- Forces and motion

- Light and sound

- The Earth and beyond.

To gain a Level 4 pupils will need to know:

- The cause and effects of physical processes. For example, a buzzer will not work when there is a break in an electrical circuit.

- Forces change the direction or speed of movement.

- The effects of light and sound, such as the way they get fainter as the sources become further away.

- How to alter electrical circuits.

- How the Sun appears to change position during the day and how shadows change as this happens.

- Objects are attracted by gravity.

- Which metals are attracted by magnets.

- Magnets can attract and repel each other.

- Sounds travel through a variety of materials, such as water, metal and wood.

When working on investigations about physical processes it is worth taking note of the following:

- Magnets can seriously damage electrical equipment such as TVs and computers.

- Never look at the Sun directly or through binoculars and telescopes. Its bright light could cause permanent damage to your eyes.

- When handling electrical equipment, make sure your hands are dry.

- Look after your ears; avoid loud sounds near your ear drums.

ANSWERS

LEVEL 4 TEST

1. d

2. b

3. c

4. They needed to keep the same: the height the gyrocopters were dropped from and the size of the gyrocopters.

5. spherical

6. false, false, true, false, true, false

7.

8. Gravity acts on the raindrops. They are pulled towards the centre of the Earth.

9. They wanted to find out if the temperature of the water made a difference to the time taken for the sugar to dissolve.

10. the temperature of the water

11. the amount of sugar, the amount of water and the person stirring

12. yes

13. 3 of: a spoon or stirring rod, stopwatch, measuring jug and thermometer

14. Boiling water is too dangerous to use in the classroom.

15. the warmer the water, the faster the sugar dissolved

16. Grace, Chantelle, Jackson, George, Kevin, Rosie

17. *Answers will vary, but could include: polar bear – white fur for camouflage, thick fur for warmth; gibbon – long arms and tail for climbing; giraffe – tall neck for reaching high leaves, spots for camouflage*

SELECTING EQUIPMENT

1. stopwatch – minutes and seconds; weighing scales – grams; forcemeter – Newtons; ruler – millimetres; tape measure – metres; thermometer – degrees Celsius; measuring jug – millilitres

2. tape measure

3. stopwatch

4. spring balance or newtonmeter/forcemeter

5. *Answers will vary.*

FINDING OUT

1. b

2. c

3. d

4. d

5. Pupils' own research into famous scientist.

PLOTTING GRAPHS

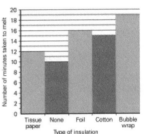

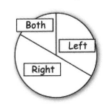

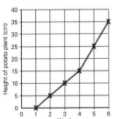

PATTERNS IN DATA

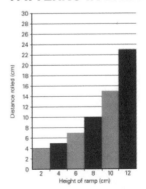

FAIR TESTING

Answers relating to the experiment to measure how quickly objects fall.

PREDICTIONS

1. Scarlett and Martin's pulse rates will gradually return to normal.

2. c

3. c

4. The paper will be weaker when wet.

5. a. Vicky

b. observations

QUESTIONS

1. c **2.** c and d

3. *Answers will vary.*

4. *Answers will vary.*

PLANT GROWTH

1. water

2. water and nutrients

3. the roots

4. to transport water and nutrients

5. b

6. c

7. to add nutrients to the soil

PARTS OF A FLOWER AND SEED DISPERSAL

1. petal

2. ovary

3. anther

4. stigma

5. stamen

6. ovule

7. *For example, any berry or fruit*

8. *For example, dandelion*

9. *For example, coconut*

THE HUMAN SKELETON

1.

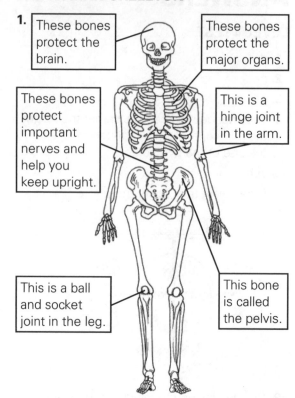

These bones protect the brain.

These bones protect the major organs.

These bones protect important nerves and help you keep upright.

This is a hinge joint in the arm.

This is a ball and socket joint in the leg.

This bone is called the pelvis.

2. to move, to support the body and to protect vital organs

LIVING PROCESSES

1. stick-insect

2. clockwork fish

3. teddy bear

4. artificial Christmas tree

5. Spot is alive because he breathes in one gas and gives out another, he has senses, gets rid of waste materials, grows, moves and feeds. (He may also be able to reproduce.)

6. *Answers will vary but could include: feeding him, giving him exercise and stimulating his senses by playing with him.*

7. The apple tree is alive because it grows, produces seeds, uses sunlight, water and air to make food and give out waste gases.

CLASSIFICATION

1. dog – mammal; hawk – bird; trout – fish; crocodile – reptile; ant – insect

2. human – mammal; ostrich – bird; shark – fish; dolphin – mammal; turtle – reptile; butterfly – insect

3. fruit bat – mammal; spider – none of these (it is an arachnid); octopus – none of these (it is a cephalopod); penguin – bird; komodo dragon – reptile

KEYS

1. a crab **b** tortoise **c** eagle **d** python

2. *Answers will vary but could include: a mussel/clam, snail/terrapin, hawk/sparrow, rattlesnake/tiger*

3. a eagle – bird **b** python – reptile **c** crab – crustacean **d** tortoise – reptile

ADAPTATION

1. Tiger – jungle – stripes… Dolphin – sea – streamlined body… Penguin – Antarctica – thick coat… Camel – desert – conserves food… Heron – riverbank – long beak… Salmon – fast-flowing river – strong tail…

2. *Answers will vary, but could include: thick coat to keep the bear warm; white fur to camouflage the bear.*

3 a. deep roots: to find water underground

b. spines: to deter predators from eating them

c. tough thick stems: to conserve water by not letting it evaporate

PREDATORS AND THEIR PREY

1. worm ➤ blackbird; rabbit ➤ fox; antelope ➤ cheetah; field mouse ➤ hawk; salmon ➤ grizzly bear; seal ➤ polar bear; water buffalo ➤ crocodile

2. a green plant

3. the sun

4. *Answers will vary.*

FOOD CHAINS

1. sun ➤ lettuce ➤ snail ➤ blackbird

2. 1 – sun; 2 – leafy plant; 3 – caterpillar; 4 – bird; 5 – cat

3. a. grass **b.** rabbit **c.** panda **d.** sun **e.** zebra **f.** seeds

4. sun ➤ plant plankton ➤ animal plankton ➤ small shrimp ➤ small fish ➤ large fish ➤ seal ➤ great white shark

MICRO-ORGANISMS

1. false

2. false

3. true

4. false

5. false

6. true

7. *Answers will vary but may include: cheese, yoghurt, beer, wine and bread.*

8. break down food into waste, extract the goodness and kill harmful microbes

THERMAL INSULATORS AND CONDUCTORS

Bronze: copper, electricity, easily, cooker, gloves, hot, materials

Silver: polystyrene, china, metal, investigation, bare, insulator

1. thermal conductor

2. thermal insulator

SOLIDS, LIQUIDS AND GASES

1. For example: diamond, iron, rock, wooden plank

2. For example: water, milk, juice, blood

3. For example: oxygen, nitrogen, helium, hydrogen

4. Solids keep their shape unless they are squashed or moved and can be cut into pieces.

5. Liquids flow and assume the shape of the container or surface which holds them.

6. Gases flow in all directions and spread out to fill the space they are in.

7. Solids: rock, butter, chocolate.

Liquids: syrup, milk, cooking oil.

Gases: oxygen, nitrogen, helium

GROUPING AND CLASSIFYING MATERIALS

1. box 1 – wool; box 2 – silk; box 3 – nylon; box 4 – cotton

2. box 1 – tissue; box 2 – kitchen roll; box 3 – greaseproof; box 4 – card

3. *Answers will vary.*

SEPARATING MIXTURES

1. magnet

2. filter

3. evaporate

4. sieve

5. *Answers will vary but could include: adding water so the sawdust will float; the salt will dissolve so you can filter the sand out and then evaporate the water to leave the salt.*

6. *Answers will vary but could include: sieving the gravel; adding water so the sugar dissolves; filtering out the sand; and letting the water evaporate to leave the sugar.*

MAKING SOLUTIONS

1. sugar, salt

2. They sank to the bottom of the container.

3. b

4. She could let the water evaporate.

5. It dissolved.

6. It evaporated.

GRAVITY

1. Gravity makes things stay on the ground and fall when they are dropped.

2. The Sun

3. Arrow should be directly beneath the sky-diver pointing to the ground.

4 a. Raincoat, bag of apples, training shoe, empty drink can.

b. gravity

5. Gravity on the Moon is a sixth of that on the Earth, so the pull towards the ground is not as strong as it is on Earth.

6. We would float off into space!

MAGNETS

1. c and f (steel and iron)

2. a. repel

b. attract

3. The magnets repelled each other.

4. The magnets would attract each other.

5.

6. *Answers will vary but you could sprinkle iron filings on a sheet of white paper then place a magnet underneath.*

ELECTRICAL CIRCUITS

1.

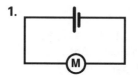

2.

3. *Answers will vary but diagram must make a full circuit without any breaks.*

SUN, EARTH AND MOON

1. spherical

2. 28

3. 365¼ days

4. the Earth spinning on its axis

5. spinning on its axis and orbiting the Sun

6. beach ball – Sun; pea – Moon; marble – Earth

7. the Sun

8. roughly 93 million miles

9. on the Moon

10. true

11. 1969

12. true

13. 13%!

AIR RESISTANCE

1. Jill hit the ground first because her parachute was 25% smaller than Jack's.

2.

3. Aeroplanes have round noses to reduce the amount of air resistance when flying.

4. The crouching skier will go faster because there will be less air resistance.

5. The lorry with the streamlined cab will use less fuel because the engine does not have to work as hard against the air resistance.

FRICTION

1. force; solid; solid; gas; liquid; heat

2. *Answers will vary but could include: grip on shoes, warming hands and tyres on cars.*

3. *Answers will vary but could include: engines wearing out, carpets being worn down and the space shuttle overheating on re-entering the Earth's atmosphere.*

4. Friction causes heat. If enough friction is generated by the two sticks rubbing together then enough heat can be generated to light some dry tinder.

5. Yachts have v-shaped prows to reduce the water resistance – the less water resistance, the faster the yacht will move through the water.

SOUND

1. vibration

2. Tick all the boxes.

3. Loud noise can damage the ears/hearing.

4. Sounds are fainter the further you are away, because as the sound travels through the air it spreads out.

5. Yes, space is a vacuum so the sound of a scream would be unable to travel.

6. a. the air   **b.** the steel rail

c. Sound travels better through solids because Beth could hear the sound through the steel rail better than through the air.

LIGHT AND SHADOW

1. the Sun, a burning candle and a lit light bulb

2. the Sun

3. opaque

4. b

5. Shadows will be shorter at midday.

6. east, west, Earth, axis

EXAM TECHNIQUES – HINTS AND TIPS

BEFORE A TEST...

- When you revise, try revising 'little and often' rather than in long chunks. This is far more productive!
- Revise with your 'revision buddy' whenever possible. You can learn from each other, spot each other's mistakes and 'test' each other.
- Make sure you are up to speed with your recall of the multiplication facts up to 10 x 10.
- Get a good night's sleep before taking a test.
- Get up in good time and eat a good breakfast (a banana makes a 'brain-friendly' snack).
- Be prepared – wear a watch so you can tell the time during your test.

DURING A TEST...

- Don't rush. Read each question twice and be clear about what you being asked to do.
- If you get stuck, don't linger too long on the same question; you can always come back to it later.
- Never leave a multiple-choice question unanswered – make a good guess at the end.
- Check to see how many marks each question is worth. Has your answer merited those marks?
- Always check your answers. Do they 'look' correct?
- Keep an eye on the time. After 20 minutes, see how far you have got.
- Leave four to five minutes at the end to go through your work. You may spot a silly mistake. Try not to leave any questions unanswered. If you really can't get the answer, then make an educated guess. Use your estimating skills!
- Always show your method or 'working out'. It may be worth a mark, even if your answer is wrong.
- Double check any calculations you do with a calculator.
- Finally, don't get stressed. Think of the test as being given the chance to show what you know.

KEY FACTS ABOUT THE SATS

- The tests take place at your school but are marked by examiners – not your teacher.
- You will get the results in July.
- Individual scores are not made public but a school's overall scores are published in what are commonly known as the 'league tables'.
- Your results will not affect your application or entry into secondary school.

REWARDS AND MOTIVATION

All children (and adults!) respond well to praise and encouragement. Talk about class/year group rewards for when the SATs are over and for individual attendance and achievement in the booster classes.

This is to certify that

_____

has attended _____ science booster lessons
(insert number)

at _____ School

and attained a

BRONZE medal

Signed _____ _Year 6 class teacher_

Signed _____ _Headteacher_

Date _____

SCHOLASTIC
www.scholastic.co.uk

This is to certify that

_____

has attended _____ science booster lessons
(insert number)

at _____ School

and attained a

SILVER medal

Signed _____ *Year 6 class teacher*

Signed _____ *Headteacher*

Date _____

This is to certify that

_____

has attended _____ science booster lessons
(insert number)

at _____ School

and attained a

GOLD medal

Signed _____ *Year 6 class teacher*

Signed _____ *Headteacher*

Date _____

SCHOLASTIC
www.scholastic.co.uk

In this series:

ISBN 978-0439-94569-1

ISBN 978-0439-94568-4

ISBN 978-0439-94513-4

ISBN 978-0439-94512-7

To find out more, call: 0845 603 9091
or visit our website www.scholastic.co.uk